METERING FOR AMERICA

METERING
FOR
AMERICA

125 Years of the Gas Industry
and American Meter Company

by Alfred Lief

APPLETON-CENTURY-CROFTS, INC.
NEW YORK

Printed in the United States of America

CONTENTS

Rembrandt Peale
a self-portrait

GAS LIGHTS

Without Oil, Tallow, Wick or Smoke.

It is not necessary to invite attention to the GAS LIGHTS by which my Saloon of Paintings it now illuminated ; those who have seen the ring beset with gems of light are sufficiently disposed to spread their reputation; the purpose of this notice is merely to say that the Museum will be illuminated EVERY EVENING until the public curiosity shall be gratified.   REMBRANDT PEALE.

june 13   eo6t

Baltimore Federal Gazette
June 13, 1816

GAS LIGHTS.

NOTICE OF THE CLOSE OF THE SEASON.

The illumination of the Museum will be continued only for a few evenings longer for this season—but as a specimen of the manner in which the Front Room will be lighted, on the commencement of the next season, a CHANDELIER of fifty burners, executed by Mr BOUIS, is placed in the Quadruped Room, which for lightness and elegance is worthy of particular attention, and calculated to display the immense superiority of the Gas Light.

Baltimore American
July 9, 1816

—1—

New Lights for Old Lamps

SAMUEL DOWN CAME FROM ENGLAND AT A CRUCIAL TIME. THE GAS business in America, in the 1830s of President Andrew Jackson, had awakened to the waste and folly of charging a flat rate per burner. Meters were needed for consumers' lines, and the only ones available had to be imported.

Down, in his twenties, got a job as a journeyman mechanic in the workshop of the Manhattan Gas-Light Company, which sold gas by the hundred cubic feet. Soon he was repairing meters for the company. He then set up his own brass foundry, supplying parts, and with his former employers' blessing he started meter manufacturing.

It was mostly handwork. The gas industry itself was still in its infancy, venturing in a few cities to displace whale-oil street lamps, and really did not begin to hit its stride in consumption until the Civil War ended. By that time Down's firm had evolved as the American Meter Company and laid the basis for concurrent growth.

Colorful individuals propelled the progress of the young nation's infant industry. The very initiator of commercial gas in this country was a portrait painter.

The scene was Baltimore, 1816. Rembrandt Peale, a son of the Philadelphia artist, Charles Willson Peale, in his youth had painted President George Washington posing in his father's museum in Philadelphia, with brothers Raphaelle, Titian, and Rubens also at easels. A few years later he accompanied his father on a dig on a Hudson Valley farm, where they unearthed mastodon bones. A skeleton was assembled for display in the Philadelphia museum. Enough bones were left over to reconstruct another mastodon, and thereby hung the tale of a chandelier of gas burners in Rembrandt Peale's Baltimore Museum and Gallery of the Fine Arts.

Enterprising Rembrandt, on learning that Rubens in Philadelphia had illuminated an exhibition room with gas distilled from pine tar by a process invented by a family friend, acquired rights for Maryland. Experiments and demonstrations of gas lighting had preceded this in other cities on the eastern seaboard after reports of success in and about London. Only two years before, the streets of St. Margaret's Parish, Westminster, had begun to be lighted by gas by a company chartered for the purpose. No such company existed in the United States—until Rembrandt Peale nourished the idea.

The artist-showman and would-be businessman had gas produced in a small building in an alley behind the museum. He piped it into a side room next to the second-floor lecture hall, the room containing "the Stupendous Skeleton of the Mammoth." On the evening of June 11, 1816, visitors to the museum on fashionable Holliday Street were treated to the spectacle of "beautiful and most brilliant light," in the words of the glowing account next day in the *Federal Gazette and Daily Advertiser*. Peale advertised, inviting others to see "the ring beset with gems of light."

He worked fast. With the enthusiastic editor of the newspaper, two prominent local businessmen, and the museum's architect, he formed a company on June 13. The same day, he presented a proposal to the mayor, who hurriedly convened a special meeting of the city council. On June 14, the editor reported that the council had named a committee which was said to be ready to recommend a franchise and a contract to light the streets. "Baltimore," said the *Federal Gazette*, "will therefore probably be the first city in the United States that will enjoy the advantage of this valuable discovery." The distinction might have been Philadelphia's, but the common council there, after taking a look at the apparatus Rubens Peale used, let the matter lie.

On June 17, ordinances were passed authorizing The Gas-Light Company of Baltimore to lay pipes under streets, lanes, and alleys and enabling the mayor to contract with it for lighting lampposts. Rembrandt Peale's vision went further. In his continuing publicity he urged citizens to observe at his museum "the new method of lighting apartments without oil, without grease, without wicks or snuffing, without smoke and with superior brilliance."

Gasworks and a square-shaped wooden holder were erected at the corner of Guilford Avenue and Saratoga Street, the architect being the company superintendent. On February 7, 1817 the first street lamp shone—just one that evening. The historic spot is at Baltimore and Holliday Streets.

Sad to say, the cradle of commercial gas rocked hard. No sooner had service begun than financial and technical troubles beset the company. Dissension and frustration caused Peale to withdraw in 1820, a year of national depression. He quit gas and Baltimore and returned to art.

Revenue from seventy customers besides the municipality hardly sufficed. The customers were mostly storekeepers who drew gas from the pipes laid for the public lamps. Most householders stuck to their tallow candles. To improve the quality of the gas, the company switched to coal as the source, but it was hampered by scanty technology and a lack of instruments as well as capital.

The most serious obstacle to wider patronage was the charge. In the absence of meters to measure the amount consumed by a user, an annual flat rate was based on an estimate for a given number of burners in a reasonable number of hours. Twelve dollars per burner appealed only to the well-to-do. Without numerous domestic consumers on service lines it would not be profitable to lay pipes in additional streets. Even so, the few people who used gas left lights burning beyond their needs, often in daytime, taking more gas than they paid for. A thrifty household had no incentive to become a customer, despite the fact that the flat rate did not pay off for the company.

While the Baltimore venture struggled along, the success of gas enterprises in England prompted formations in other American cities. The Boston Gas-Light Company was organized in 1822, when the town of Boston became a city. It received a charter the next year, but some time elapsed before starting construction of a plant. New Year's Day 1829 brought gaslight to Dock Square. New York moved faster.

Capitalists who had been blocked earlier by oil and tallow interests, but in 1823 obtained a franchise for their New York Gas-Light Company, at once dispatched their superintendent to England. He was instructed to consult the pioneering gas engineers there, send back equipment, and learn how the operating

Consumer bill, 1826: $1 per 100 cu. ft. plus meter and fixture rent

companies prevented the waste of gas. In his report he recommended "the use of Gas meters to measure the supply of Gas to customers, and a large one to register the quantity made at the station before it is conveyed to Gasometers [holders]."

Subscribers to service were signed up at one dollar per hundred cubic feet, plus a rental charge for the meters. Broadway, from the Battery to Grand Street, was to be the first line of march for the men who must dig and lay cast-iron mains as prescribed by the city corporation. Dwellings and stores on lower Broadway, the "best part of town" (total city population, about 145,000), put aside their smelly whale-oil lamps early in 1825 and let the company worry about manufacturing gas from this oil. By fall there were 1700 burners installed and a growing waiting list.

The New York company made a profit from the start, although the station meter showed that oil was expensive for the quantity of gas it yielded. Consumer meters, like the station meter, were of the wet type, using water as a seal. Their construction was simple: a cylindrical case containing a partitioned drum filled with water to a little above the center. Gas entering from the inlet exerted pressure on the partitions, and as they alternately received and delivered, the drum revolved and passed the gas to the outlet. Since the cubical contents of the compartments were known, an index counting the revolutions measured the amount of gas released.

The device, made in England, was so accurate it was the most dependable instrument in laboratory work. But in order to obtain

correct registration, the water level had to remain constant. This
meant guarding against evaporation in hot weather and freeze in
winter. To meet the latter hazard, the water was spiked with
alcohol; the company obligingly supplied customers with whiskey
at a dollar for four gallons. What sometimes happened to the
whiskey was a matter of private concern.

For all its drawbacks—need of repair, high maintenance costs—
the wet meter of that day performed its appointed function. The
company billed the customer for what it sold, and he paid only
for what he consumed. Increased consumption occasioned a cut
in price to ninety cents per hundred cubic feet in 1828, and conversion of the plant to manufacture gas from rosin made possible
another ten-cent reduction in 1829.

Helping to heighten the popularity of gaslight was a decision
of the common council to install lamps all along Broadway up to
Grand Street, which inspired the phrase "Great White Way" and
stirred residents and merchants on other streets to petition for the
modern service. As the sales volume rose, the rate went down
again. And with the city's population spreading northward, an-

"The Great White Way"—Broadway, New York, 1828
(Contemporary print)

other market opened. A second group of entrepreneurs, the Manhattan Gas-Light Company, moved into it with a franchise in 1833 to operate above Grand Street.

The same year, the directors of the company in Baltimore came to a realistic conclusion: the only way to get more customers on more mains (scarcely two miles so far) was to lower the price, and the only way to make money was to adopt meters. Customers who had been using gas freely took umbrage at the announced intention. They held a protest rally in a hotel and adopted resolutions denouncing the plan. An ordinance was introduced in the council to prohibit the sale of gas by the cubic foot.

The Baltimore company published a rejoinder. It had never intended unrestricted use. Rates originally had been determined by the size of the burners, the height of the flame, and a definite time. Lights were supposed to be extinguished by 10:00 or 11:00 P.M., not burn all night and all day; and the perforations weren't supposed to be enlarged, nor the burners taken off the ends of the gas pipes. Since correct measurement was now possible, by meters whose accuracy was tested by apparatus at the works, a fair price could be charged—far below New York and Boston prices—and both parties would benefit. Unless all consumers had meters on their premises, a perfect light would not be obtained for lack of regular and sufficient pressure. "The principal benefit which the Company expect to derive from the general use of meters is the prevention of waste; but they expect also . . . to obtain a considerable class of consumers who want the gas occasionally and are precluded from using it at all because there is no accurate mode of ascertaining the quantity except by meter. . . ."

The hostile ordinance failed to pass. Wet meters were ordered from England, the source also of fixtures, and consumers soon received their gas at forty cents per hundred cubic feet and a monthly meter rental of seventeen cents. This was not the last to be heard, however, in complaint or jest about the gas meter, that silent, unperturbed guardian of the common interests of company and customer. For the Baltimore management the transition marked a turning point, the beginning of prosperity as increasing business came in on a sound financial basis.

Needing meters, the Baltimore company thought it might as well look for them at home, for two local machinists, Samuel Hills and John Rodgers, independently were experimenting along this

line. A contract was given to Rodgers. Unequal to the task, he
engaged John M. Slaney, Sr., a former employee of Clegg &
Crosley, London's leading meter makers. Baltimore thereby added
another American first to its laurels in the tradition of Peale, the
premature pioneer.

A further sign of initiative on the part of the Baltimore gas
company's management was a decision to make chandeliers and
brackets in its own shop, along with copper service pipes, fittings,
and other items required for distribution. It called Slaney into the
shop to superintend the production and repair of meters. Here he
remained while his apprenticed son learned the trade and left to
form a partnership, Collier & Slaney, Jr., adopting as their meter
badge a shield surmounted by an eagle. With gas companies
springing up in various cities, a market was developing for the
American article. Eventually the Slaneys organized a new firm,
the Phoenix Meter Company; their badge, a phoenix hovering
over flames—gas flames, no doubt.

One day, when Slaney senior was still employed in the shop,
a visitor dropped in who had worked beside him at Clegg &
Crosley. His name was Theophilus P. Code. An ambitious man,
Code had not been able to see meters being exported to the States
without determining to export his talents. After setting foot in
New York, he worked on meter repairs at the Manhattan Gas-
Light Company, where Samuel Down met him. Code stayed but
briefly, for he wanted to be a manufacturer. On his visit to Slaney,
he mentioned the new gasworks in Philadelphia and said he intended to go there and show his skill.

The Philadelphia story reopened in the same year New York
got its second gas company and Baltimore overcame flat rates,

Collier & Slaney, Jr.   Samuel Down   Phoenix

EARLY METER BADGES

Philadelphia Gas Works
built in 1835

1833. This was a coincidence with a difference, for the burning issue with alarmed Philadelphians was whether they should have gas at all. They addressed "A Remonstrance" to the city councils, declaring gas "most inexpedient and dangerous . . . as ignitable as gunpowder and nearly as fatal." Adding insult to alleged injury, the document went on, "It is also an uncertain light, sometimes suddenly disappearing and leaving the streets and houses in total darkness." The councils nevertheless had an investigation made in Europe and resolved the next year to build a municipal facility. Philadelphia certainly was different!

A station erected at 22nd and Market Streets started up in February 1836, serving a small number of consumers initially at thirty-five cents per hundred cubic feet on imported meters. Possibly patriotism, at any rate the still flourishing spirit of independence, led to an apologetic note in a report of the appointive board who ran the Philadelphia Gas Works: "Notwithstanding the desire of the trustees to procure meters of American Manufacture, they found themselves obliged to resort again to England for this year's supply," meaning 1837. Then Theophilus Code appeared on the scene.

Code learned from Philadelphia's engineer that a trial order had been placed with an influential but inexperienced person. Not one to be thwarted easily, Code proceeded to demonstrate his ability by building a meter in a blacksmith's shop. The sequel: the other man, Owen Colton, teamed up with him as Colton & Code. The trustee's report for 1839 said, "The meters furnished by one of our fellow citizens, thus far, proved highly satisfactory, and, as yet, there has appeared no reason to doubt that they are equal to those introduced from abroad."

The promise being fulfilled, the performance of Colton & Code signalized the advent of a lively meter industry in Philadelphia. This firm became Code & Hopper, later Code, Hopper & Gratz, in time forming a union with Down in New York; while in the interim a competing company arose in Philadelphia which was to spawn eight others.

In New York the population surge favored the growth of the Manhattan Gas-Light Company. Its station, producing coal gas (coke for sale), was on West 18th Street near the North River (the Hudson). Its rising star was Charles Roome, who started as a junior clerk, studied civil engineering at night, and became Manhattan's engineer; in time also its astute president and an outstanding figure in the councils of the country's gas business. Roome recognized superior qualities in Down, as to mechanical skill, energy, and judgment, and urged him in 1836 to go into manufacturing complete meters.

Down did well. First in a factory a block away from Manhattan's station, and by 1847 in a large new factory on West 22nd Street and North River, with his dwelling in back, facing 21st Street, he enjoyed the entire meter business not only of the Manhattan but also of the New York Company. A new customer was

Nightfall in New York, 1837: lamplighter at work.
St. Thomas Church on lower Broadway

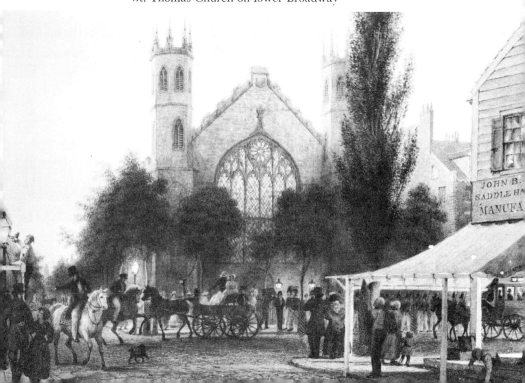

the Brooklyn Gas-Light Company, founded in 1825, but starting service in 1849. Orders came in from other cities and the British Provinces (i.e., Canada) as Down won the confidence of gas company officers. He had a full line of apparatus essential to gas engineers, such as station meters, pressure registers, pressure indicators and gauges, photometers to test the candlepower of gas, and provers to test the calibration of meters.

Among the first makers to appreciate the value of dry meters following their development in England, Down displayed his "improved dry gas-meter" at the World's Fair of 1853, held in the New York Crystal Palace. This large structure of iron frames and glass, on the present site of Bryant Park, was illuminated by gas —measured by his new meter.

Wet meters were incurring dissatisfaction, not as to accuracy but because of occasional failure due to weather and the inconvenience of attending them. Also, they cost too much for the volume of gas they purveyed. The acknowledged father of the wet meter, Samuel Clegg, in London, had indeed first attempted to make a dry meter. An American inventor and manufacturer, James Bogardus, also tried, using the pressure of gas on oiled-silk diaphragms, instead of a drum, and valves as the seal in place of water, placing the mechanism in a rectangular tin case in 1833. Bogardus might have been credited with paternity of the dry meter except that his device proved unreliable. The diaphragms moved unsteadily, so that displacement of gas was not uniform, and the valves caused so much friction as to retard the flow.

Bogardus made some corrections, but another American, William Richards, working with a London manufacturer, did better. Richards' stepping-stone was a meter with three square diaphragms and rotary valves. He substituted two round leather diaphragms and sliding valves, thereby achieving positive displacement in 1843. Thomas Glover, of London, perfected this invention and manufactured it with an index geared to diaphragm movements to register the cubic feet passing through the meter. Here was the prototype of the gas industry's cash register. British companies were slow to switch from the wet type, but American conditions favored quicker interest. Down's adaptation of the Glover meter was one of the modifications brought out by meter makers in this country.

Bogardus caught sight of Down's meter at the World's Fair

Samuel Down

Manhattan Gas-Light Company: the works on West 18th Street and the photometer room, depicted in *Harper's Monthly*, 1862, with a Samuel Down dry meter *(right)*.

Charles Roome

and was surprised. He called on Charles Roome and learned that dry meters were an accepted measuring instrument in England, where he had failed to get a patent. Bogardus then took his grief to Down, who offered him a large sum if he could get an extension of his American patent. The inventor tried, but it was too late.

Even so, dry meters were not yet adopted generally. An objection was that gas condensates accumulated in the meter, causing inaccurate measurement. Down's answer was to insert a drip pipe at the inlet and outlet. "When the accumulation reaches a certain point," he explained, "the flow of gas is stopped and the condensable matter must be removed before the lights can be restored."

He disparaged the use of rotary valves by other makers and pointed to unhappy English experience. Slide valves were the standard. He claimed for an eccentric slide valve that he patented that it was self-cleansing and leak-proof and "the Meter to which it is attached will not vary in its registration more than one-half of one per cent."

Although Down still made wet meters, he promoted the dry type as the meter of the future. He gave his New York gas company customers as references. A third gas company in the city, formed in 1855 to serve the sparsely settled area north of 79th Street, started afresh. This was the Harlem Gas-Light Company, the first to introduce dry meters throughout its territory.

Down had two or three competitors in New York, all small and short-lived; but in the bid for the patronage of the 381 gas companies in the United States in 1860, out-of-town makers were factors to consider.

In Boston, the name of Nathaniel Tufts emerged. Foreman of a meter company organized in 1849 by the head of the Boston Gas-Light Company, he turned out wet meters and ventured with dry ones. The shop failed. Tufts entered into general manufacturing in 1860 with the Tufts-Cheever Company, his partners attending to ships' lanterns and to churns while he concentrated on meters.

In Albany, the last of the oil lamps had faded from the streets but recently, and the local gas company had just reduced its price per cubic foot, when two brothers opened a meter business—D. & H. McDonald, 1855. They made the wet type in cast-iron cases. The results were disappointing, and brother Hugh dropped out.

Nathaniel Tufts   Donald McDonald I

Where the first gaslights were turned on in Rochester, New York, 1848:
front parlor of Nehemiah Osburn, whose firm contracted to lay the mains

Brother Donald, instead, looked into dry meters and went to England for a closer look. On returning to Albany he began putting diaphragms and valves together, trading as D. McDonald & Company in 1858 and challenging the older houses with a full line of apparatus. "The extreme simplicity of our Dry Meters renders their wear and liability to get out of order less than any other Meter in the market."

In Baltimore, financial collapse of the Phoenix in 1859, after nine years of filling orders from many states and the West Indies, marked the end of an era, the beginning of another. Thomas Tansley, a watchmaker on Phoenix movements, joined with Edwin Baker, a meter maker from Philadelphia, and operated on a small scale. Short of capital, they advertised for it. This appeal was what later brought Charles E. Dickey and following him his son, Charles H. Dickey, into the world of gas meters.

The strong competition at present was in Philadelphia. Theophilus Code had taken the Hopper family into the picture, and by 1859 the firm name was Code, Hopper & Gratz, on Filbert Street, the direction falling to Thomas C. Hopper and Robert H. Gratz. Their production was large. They patented improvements, one patent covering meter fittings; another, assigned by the inventor to Gratz, improved the rotary valve of a three-diaphragm meter.

Also in Philadelphia, Washington Harris was a vigorous contender, his experience dating back to 1848. His firm became Harris & Brother, with a factory on Cherry Street, de-emphasizing wet meters in 1859 after a visit from England by Thomas Glover. Harris, too, patented an improved dry meter.

Code, Hopper & Gratz vied with Samuel Down in making the broadest advertising claims. Said the Philadelphians, "We have manufactured a larger number of Gas Meters than any other establishment in the world." Said Down of himself, "His present factory . . . he believes . . . is the most complete and extensive . . . in the world, and his machinery for gas meter making far in advance, in all the new improvements, of any other manufacturer's in the country."

In the midst of the battle of superlatives a newcomer slipped onto the scene in New York: John J. Griffin, a machinist by training. He started making meters in 1859 and proceeded with persistence and a vision of greatness, ultimately taking in as a junior partner his son-in-law, John Gribbel.

SAMUEL DOWN,

os. 340, 342, 344 AND 346 WEST TWENTY-SECOND STREET,

NORTH RIVER, NEW YORK.

MANUFACTURER OF

WET AND DRY PATENT GAS METERS,

essure Registers, Pressure Indicators and Gauges, Station, Show, Customer and Experimenting Meters, and the Celebrated Testing Gas Holders *
now used in the State of New York, in compliance
with an Act of the Legislature.

ALSO,

THE PHOTOMETRICAL APPARATUS.

NEW YORK, June 25. 1859.

Mr. Down embraces this opportunity of returning his thanks to the Gas-Light Companies, Gas Engineers, consumers generally, of the United States, the British Provinces, South America and Cuba, for the very eral patronage he has received from them the past year, which has *greatly exceeded his most sanguine calcu-ons;* the demand for his IMPROVED PATENT DRY GAS METERS having been, by *many thousands,* greater than previous year. Mr. Down being a *practical mechanic,* and having given his *entire attention,* for over ITEEN YEARS, to the manufacture and improvement of Gas Meters, claims, without fear of contradiction, periority for the Gas Meters manufactured by him over all others in the country, for the proof of which would simply revert to the fact that he has always manufactured for the *Manhattan and New York Gas-ht Companies all the meters used by them;* and at present is also manufacturing meters for the most ensive companies in the Union, the British Provinces, South America and Cuba. *All meters manufactured him are tested and sealed by the Gas Meter Inspector of the State, appointed by the Governor under the act he last Legislature.* His present factory was erected in 1847, and he believes it is the most complete and ensive at present in the world, and his machinery for gas meter making far in advance, in all the new provements, of any other manufacturer's in the country. He therefore deems it highly necessary to place s-Light Companies throughout the Union, British Provinces, South America and Cuba *on their guard* against parties who are so industriously endeavoring to introduce to their notice PATENT DRY GAS METERS, *con-ucted precisely in imitation of his;* but with *Chinese-like characteristics,* without fully understanding the rect principles upon which they are made. Mr. Down respectfully invites purchasers to visit for pection, at any time, his works and the materials used by him in his manufacture of Gas Meters, feeling ured that the result of such inspection will be the *undoubted conviction* of the correctness of his statement.

In conclusion, he would state that he is now prepared to manufacture the PHOTOMETRICAL APPARATUS ording to the correct ENGLISH STANDARD, and will furnish, gratuitously, the directions for arranging the otometer Room and the rules for the proper working of the apparatus.

Mr. Down is fully prepared at all times to execute, upon the shortest notice, all orders for Gas ters, wet and dry, and the Photometer Apparatus, with the guarantee of entire satisfaction.
Illustrative Electrotypes will appear in the second number of the American Gas-Light Journal.

* The standard of measurement of this Gas-holder is given by Professors Torrey, of the Assay Office; Joy, of Columbia College; Gibbs, of the Free demy, with several other distinguished scientific gentlemen.

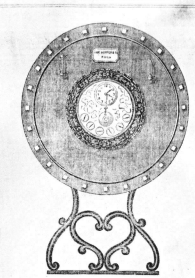
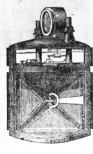

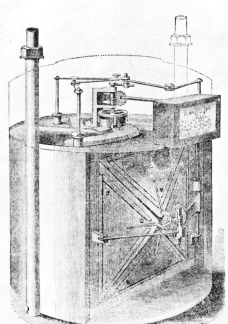

More than mere suppliers, those who provided the apparatus and instruments indispensable to the functioning of the gas companies were technically informed helpmates in the utilities' progress. The meter houses constituted a branch of the gas engineering profession, and in striving to outdo each other they contributed to the business of making and selling gas. The stage was set for collaboration through all the vicissitudes to come.

In the changeover of consumer meters, the gas company employee who handled the job was a familiar sight on city streets, going afoot from house to house laden with his materials. On a cord suspended from his shoulders and back he carried as many meters, lead connections, and wooden shelves as he could bear —and his tools. Sometimes this gave the appearance of a pack mule with a walrus mustache. The "meter man" went down into the basement, replaced the old device, and knew he wouldn't have to come round again to fill the meter with water so as not to run slow; and maybe wistfully reflected that when winter came he wouldn't be there to whiskey the meter.

Still, attempts were made to retain the wet type. To help the die-hards, an inventor offered a "reconciler" attachment that made the water level self-adjusting. "A child that can carry a small pitcher of water can fill a meter as well as the most experienced gas-engineer." Some firms offered patented non-freezing, non-evaporating fluids.

Ideas abounded. A manufacturer of mailboxes for lampposts— "protected by light day and night"—advertised an improved method of setting meters on the outside of houses. "The burglars need no longer gain admittance to dwellings under pretense of examining the meters, while they, in fact, examine the fastenings. The meter-box, being neatly and securely imbedded in the front wall, the meter is protected against frost by means of a thick pad on the back of the door."

Of prime concern was the consumer meter's accuracy, at once the safeguard of a gas company's net income and subject-matter for state legislation. The public interest took form in a New York statute in 1859 providing for an inspector. After the effective date, no meter could be placed in service without his seal of approval. Gas companies were required to have on hand suitable testing apparatus, and the inspector's salary was to be apportioned among them. Complaining consumers were entitled to demand a check-up, at their company's expense if the meter was found faulty in their disfavor; but if not, they must pay the expense of removal, proving, and reinstallation. Two years later, Massachusetts passed a law for inspection both of meters and of gas. It specified an illumination standard of twelve candlepower.

Human nature having a capacity for resentment, the meter-box in many a home was considered no friend of the family. People who chafed at paying a rental for this ally of the bill collector bombarded the New York legislature with complaints. They posed the question, Would it be reasonable for a dealer in dry goods or groceries to charge for the use of his measure? Charles Roome, now president of the Manhattan company, defended rent on the ground that it was an element in cost of service; it involved interest on the expense of purchasing, servicing, and repairing meters. Legislation was staved off. The three New York City companies abolished meter rentals early in 1861, while a fourth, the Metropolitan, which was seeking entry, pledged itself to future users never to charge for meters or service connections.

The uneasy feeling about lawmakers was reflected in a lampoon on Congress published in *The American Gas-Light Journal* on the opening of a new session in this time of strain between the North and the South. Congress was designated as "the Great National Gas Works"; the Capitol, "the grand national gas-holder." Senators were mains emanating from retort houses (state legislatures), while Representatives were so many service pipes. The gas they emitted was unreliable; sometimes explosive, patriotic gas, or harmless (buncombe), but much was malodorous. "The smell from this gas is now suffocating the Union. We hope that in mercy some of the gas men of Washington will vary the charges of their local retorts and give us a different flavor during the remainder of the session."

Unfortunately, great national issues could not be resolved by amusing metaphor. The Civil War broke out and divided the nation.

Business felt the blow of war, the gas business no exception. As the cost of coal, metals, and other materials rose, gas companies refrained from expanding and cut back their normal operations. Some companies actually got started during the war, but after long preparations. The Peoples Gas-Light and Coke Company, at last financed in 1861, shared Chicago with a small com-

[Handwritten letter from Abraham Lincoln:]

Executive Mansion
Washington, Jan. 10, 1865

Mr. J. W. Garrett
    My dear Sir.

        It is said we shall
soon all be in the dark
here, unless you can bring coal
to make gas. I suppose you
would do this, without my inter-
ference, if you could; and I
only write now to say, it is very
important to me, and not to
say that you must neglect the supplying the army to promote this, or
to carry coal. Do all you
can for me in both matters.

                    Yours truly,
                    A. Lincoln

President Lincoln's appeal to the Baltimore & Ohio Railroad to deliver coal to Washington for gaslight during the Civil War

pany founded in the frontier town in 1850. The Metropolitan in New York acquired the district between 34th and 79th Streets from the Manhattan and commenced service in 1863. Some companies managed to raise rates; the Manhattan, precluded from this by the terms of its franchise, resumed meter rents. All that were dependent upon coal suffered either from shortage or from stoppage.

Coal deliveries from Pennsylvania on occasion were held up and mining halted, because of priority for the transport of troops and supplies. President Lincoln urged the head of the Baltimore & Ohio Railroad to do his best: "It is said we shall soon all be in the dark here, unless you can bring coal to make gas." To make

Thaddeus S. C. Lowe, gas apparatus inventor, ascending in his balloon *Intrepid* to observe Confederate batteries at Yorktown, 1862

matters worse, even for gas companies able to procure coal from Nova Scotia, the market was flooded with kerosene. This commodity, thanks to strikes of oil in Titusville, Pennsylvania, and its environs, found a welcome in homes. Filling the old lamp with kerosene was cheaper than using gas.

The meter business severely felt the impact of wartime conditions. Higher manufacturing costs and lower demand made survival barely possible. As it happened, just before the war Samuel Down had been persuaded by Joseph Sabbaton, Manhattan Gas-Light's engineer, to take in a partner. He was Richard Merrifield, secretary of the Albany Gas-Light Company and Sabbaton's brother-in-law. The firm became Down & Merrifield in 1861. A change occurred also in Philadelphia, this one a split. Robert H. Gratz & Company emerged, leaving behind Code, Hopper & Company in 1862. As the war dragged on another year, difficulties increased for all three concerns, not to mention smaller meter houses nor overlook the effect of foreign competition.

The Philadelphians decided to heal their wounds and approach the New Yorkers together with a proposal. Their logic was appealing. In 1863 the three companies merged and incorporated as American Meter Company under a fifty-year New York charter. Code, Hopper furnished $10,625 of the cash capital, Down & Merrifield $9375, and Gratz the rest for a total of $25,000. Samuel Down became president. The other officers were Henry Cartwright, of Code, Hopper, vice president; and Richard Merrifield, secretary and treasurer. Factories were to continue in both cities. Just as the war was being fought to preserve the Union, so the parties found that in union there was strength.

Help came from Washington. Congress, seeking revenues to carry on the struggle in 1864, raised import duties, and in scanning the list of duty-free articles selected gas meters for a tariff of 40 per cent ad valorem. With this support the manufacturers were able to meet their hardships more heartily. They produced in large volume as imports declined, and gradually they lowered the price of meters, so that it finally fell below the price of those sold in England.

Still another circumstance during the Civil War affected the gas industry. It concerned a balloonist who made observations for the Army of the Potomac. It was while generating hydrogen gas behind the lines that Thaddeus S. C. Lowe got the idea for a generator-superheater, the basis of a water-gas process which was to supplant coal gas with its higher illuminating power.

—2—

Cooking With Gas

THE INQUIRING, SCIENTIFIC MIND OF THADDEUS LOWE BECAME INTER-
ested in ballooning when ascensions at county fairs were a popular sport. *The American Gas-Light Journal* prophesied before the
Civil War that the day was not distant when every small town
would have a coal-gas plant with facilities for inflating balloons
for personal transportation—a trip in a one-man balloon would be
as ordinary as a buggy ride. Lowe went aloft to study air currents.

After serving as chief aeronaut in the Union Army, he experimented on producing gas by the interaction of steam and incandescent carbon, substituting a superheater and a carburetor for
the customary retort used in distillation of coal. Other scientists
too were trying to make water gas for a brighter flame and more
gas at less cost; but Lowe's process had the merit of being commercially feasible. His first water-gas apparatus was erected in
1873 at Phoenixville, Pennsylvania. This marked the onset of the
most important development in gas manufacturing.

There were nearly a thousand gasworks in the country at the
time of the United States Centennial Exhibition in Philadelphia
in 1876. The population had doubled in the last two decades and
thriving cities dotted the hinterland. Kerosene had lost its bid to
become the household illuminant where gas service was accessible. The sale of Procter & Gamble candles had begun to decline
(William Procter grudgingly admitted gaslights into his Cincinnati home). To illustrate advances made in gas engineering over
the years, the American Society of Civil Engineers solicited exhibits for display at the Philadelphia centennial.

Visitors to the exhibition gazed at an array of gas lighting fixtures of American manufacture in the main aisle of the main
building. This showing manifested, according to a guidebook, "to
what a surprising extent the taste of our people for luxury and

Explanation of the Meter, Indexes, &c.

The outer case of the Wet Meter has inclosed in it a cylinder or Drum, divided into four compartments, each holding a certain proportion of a cubic foot. The revolution of the Drum on its axis when the Gas is turned on, gives the motion to the wheel-work of the Index, according to the number of cubic feet delivered. In the Dry Meter, the measurement is effected by compartments having flexible joints, by whose motion the quantity delivered is shown on the Index.

ON THE ONE CIRCLE DIAL,

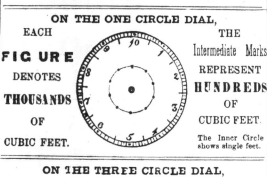

EACH **FIGURE** DENOTES **THOUSANDS** OF CUBIC FEET.

THE Intermediate Marks REPRESENT **HUNDREDS** OF CUBIC FEET.

The Inner Circle shows single feet.

ON THE THREE CIRCLE DIAL,

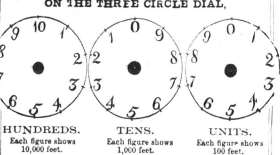

HUNDREDS.	TENS.	UNITS.
Each figure shows 10,000 feet.	Each figure shows 1,000 feet.	Each figure shows 100 feet.

Deduct the index of the former inspection from the present index, and the difference is the quantity which has been supplied in the intermediate time.

In order to fill the Wet Meter properly, to remedy deficiency of light, the main-cock should be turned off, the top, side, and bottom screws taken out, and the liquid gently poured in until it drips at the side opening; the screws being then securely replaced, and the cock turned on, a full supply will be obtained in a few seconds. Care must be taken not to bring a light near the Meter.

In Cold Weather, the Meter and Service Pipe should be protected by suitable covering from the action of the frost and thus the inconvenience of the light going out from that cause will be prevented. The Inspectors are instructed to substitute alcohol for water in the Meters, when furnished with the article by and at the expense of the consumer. The ordinary kind of Whisky will answer the purpose.

When a smell of Gas is perceived, no light must be taken near the place where the escape is, especially if the situation be confined. Notice should be sent to the Company. Free ventilation should be resorted to, and, as an additional precaution, the stop-cock at the Meter should be shut.

Reverse side of a gas bill in the 1860s: instructions on the care of wet meters in cold weather specify "the ordinary kind of Whisky" at the consumer's expense

Oldtime meter setter with wet and dry types; *(below)* inspector bent on keeping meters from freezing

variety has gone in the single direction of apparatus for light."
More startling were gas stoves. Exhibitors demonstrated to awed
audiences cooking methods that could emancipate family members from the chores of carrying fuel, feeding the fire, and hauling out ashes.

Those who entered the immense Machinery Hall saw the kinds
of machines the gas industry utilized. Following the guidebook
to a collection of meters, and keeping up with its humor, readers
noted: "The whole system of registering the consumption of gas
is shown, but we are not treated to an exhibit of the method of
making a meter register more gas than is burned. That is a secret
which the gas companies do not care to make public."

In this hall meter makers vied for attention with exhibits of
various products and for an award from the Centennial Commission, which would have much advertising value. The judges, who
included Professor Joseph Henry, secretary of the Smithsonian
Institution, went the rounds and wrote a citation: "The instruments are well made, reliable as to indication, and embody a
number of sundry improvements. . . ." Winner of the accolade
and a gold medallion was the Philadelphia firm of Harris, Griffin
and Company.

In the lively business of supplying appliances to the gas companies, Harris, Griffin was an offshoot of Harris & Brother. One
of the Harrises had broken away to operate separately. John J.
Griffin had come from New York in 1869 to join forces and patents
with him. And they prospered.

Another man of ambition who left Harris & Brother to establish
a new badge was William W. Goodwin, selling his interest in
Harris in 1872 to William Helme. Although a new man in meters,
Helme enjoyed fame as a constructor of gasworks in Southern
cities and was a large stockholder in the first Atlanta gas enter-
prise; he rebuilt it after Sherman's march to the sea. Called to a
meeting in New York, presided over by Charles Roome, Helme
helped found the American Gas-Light Association in 1873.

Three years later John McIlhenny, whose familiarity with
meters dated back to an apprenticeship at Colton & Code, returned to Philadelphia after a career, like Helme's, of building
gasworks in the South (and serving five terms as mayor of Columbus, Georgia). He bought an interest in Harris & Brother, and the
upshot was Harris, Helme & McIlhenny.

EARLY FACTORIES

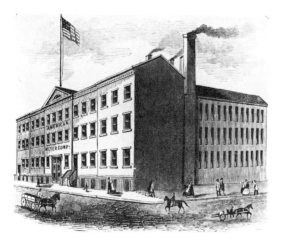

American Meter
New York

American Meter
Philadelphia

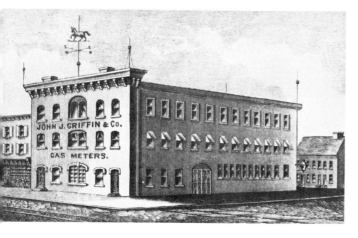

John J. Griffin & Co.
Philadelphia

3-lt. wet meter
Samuel Down

3-diaphragm exhibition meter
Samuel Down

McDonald wet meter
Serial No. 2, 1855

2-diaphragm Tufts meter
1860

2-lt. wet meter, American Meter
registered in cents

Besides these competitors of the American Meter Company in Philadelphia, and numerous small houses elsewhere, a formidable firm was rising in Baltimore. Banker Charles E. Dickey became so fascinated with meters that he lent his name to the meter business in which he invested: Dickey, Baker & Company (1866), Dickey, Tansley & Company (1875). The badge they adopted and promoted was Maryland Meter.

American Meter had grown fast after the war and required larger floorspace. In Philadelphia the Hopper family built a new factory at 22nd and Arch Streets and rented it to the company. Samuel Down added a floor to the already large New York factory building, which he personally owned, and also rented it. An agent appointed in Boston invaded the Tufts' territory. Other agencies were set up in Cincinnati and St. Louis. Later, Thomas C. Hopper, general superintendent, journeyed to California to call on gas companies and arrange for representation in San Francisco. When Down died in 1876 at the age of sixty-three, Hopper became president.

Of Down, Roome said, "He was a high-toned and most honorable man. It was impossible to know him intimately and not to love him." Of the company, he said it "put a stop to the importation of gas meters from Europe." Reverting to the man as a mechanic of superior skill and judgment, Roome declared, "In all the improvements which have taken place in this branch of our profession, the clear head and careful observations of Samuel Down can be distinctly traced."

Innumerable designs of dry meters had been introduced by various makers in Down's period, new ones still appearing. There were reversions to three diaphragms and square diaphragms, innovations such as plunger-type diaphragms, conical valves, elliptic valves, square and eccentric rotary valves. Many models of the time were "fearful and wonderful," to quote a retrospective commentator, Donald McDonald II. His grandfather had brought out a square-diaphragm three-light meter, which at least surpassed its rivals with a rated capacity of seventy-eight cubic feet an hour. The variations in forms of mechanical motion had a common purpose in a rush to keep pace with the greater demands of the gas industry. But after all, the simplicity of the Glover type remained the criterion of consumer meters (not only then, but down to the present day).

The mechanical principle employed was universal. Given the volume of gas needed to inflate and deflate a diaphragm completely, the mechanism registered the number of times the gas was expelled. In a well-made meter the motions were positive. What a dry meter offered over and above the accuracy of a wet meter was dependability. In addition, it afforded purchase by utilities at a lower cost.

The British nomenclature for size designations persisted. Originally, rated capacity was based on the standard English burner consuming six cubic feet an hour. Thus a three-light meter passed eighteen cubic feet, a five-light thirty, and so on. These sizes continued in usage though actual capacities had long since been increased.

With the advent of water-gas systems, meters were subjected to a fresh problem in the chemistry of gas.

The Lowe process made its first big impression in Baltimore. A new gas company brought it in, promising lower price and better light. Lowe's associate on installation jobs (who, by the way, eyewitnessed Confederate firing on Lowe's balloon at Yorktown) put up the new works in 1878. A price war ensued, resulting in a gain of many customers for all three companies in Baltimore, and shortly in consolidation, with price stabilized at $2.00 per thousand cubic feet instead of $2.50. Further competition arose, involving other processes, but water-gas production was extended.

In New York the pattern was much the same, only more complex. A company with a roving franchise and a patent for making water gas, a second new company with its own patent, and still another that distributed water gas, broke into the expanding city and into the realms of the Manhattan, New York, and Harlem companies. Consumers switched to water gas, and meters with them.

Across the United States coal gas began to be supplanted in one plant after another. Lowe had a firm in Norristown, Pennsylvania, manufacturing water-gas sets. The United Gas Improvement Company in Philadelphia pushed their sale and installation, and other systems contributed to the conversion.

The problem that developed in the early years of water gas had to do with meter diaphragms. Production methods, which included vaporization and assimilation of oil, introduced vapors

Thaddeus S. C. Lowe

Patent Office model of the original Lowe carburetted water-gas apparatus, 1872; generator and superheater

of heavy hydrocarbons in the flow of gas. Gum-forming and corrosive impurities condensed on the smooth, supple diaphragm skins and absorbed the animal oils worked into them. The leather became stiff, shrank, and restricted displacement, making a meter run fast. Meters returned for repair exposed diaphragms that were tarred if not water-soaked; others so deteriorated as to be porous or cracked, permitting gas to bypass and causing registration to be slow.

To cope with the situation, meter makers revised their formulas for the preparation and preservation of the leather, so it could withstand the detrimental elements. Gas makers applied themselves also and by eliminating erroneous practices succeeded in producing water gas that was fixed in character and quality.

The ultimate goal was consumer satisfaction. Householders had been relieved of charges for putting in service connections and the necessity of going to a gas fitter to have their meters set and in some cases paying for a meter shelf. Meter rental, too, was out. Gas rates were lower than ever, but suspicion of bills did not diminish. The meter was still widely regarded as an accomplice of the gas company.

Controversies over bills were enlivened by journalistic jabs. "It is an insult to a respectable citizen," a writer observed, "to take the word of a pot-bellied object of green tin, with its expressionless face, in preference to his own, threatening to leave him in the dark because the thing accuses him of having consumed gas that he knows, and the company knows, he did not consume."

"I have some very worthy customers," the superintendent of the Knoxville (Tennessee) Gas Light Company wrote in a letter-to-the-editor, "who gravely persist in calling it the 'meteor.' No doubt they think it somewhat akin to those transitory bodies, an idea derived and fostered probably from the general verdict of 'fastness' with which these ingenious and truthful pieces of mechanism seem to be endowed."

A Sunday story for the consolation of readers of a New York newspaper told about a man who trained "gas dogs," and of folks "who make it a point to remain at home all day on the day when the gas inspector is expected, merely to enjoy the yell of the inspector when the gas dog's teeth go into his calf. . . . An amiable Christian lady residing in Thirty-fifth Street has no less than forty-three samples of trousers collected by her gas dog in the course of five years."

The trouble was, observed the Knoxville superintendent, the meter was a public mystery. Most consumers could as easily translate a passage in Sanskrit as read an index. They seldom saw it, since it was tucked away in an inaccessible corner of the cellar. He blamed architects for not providing a proper place; they should ascertain the size required and specify a recess, say in the main hall or entrance of a home, and cover the recess with a glass door ornamented to taste. Each morning the consumer could see the amount of gas burned the night before, having learned with a little practice to read the dials as expertly as tell the time of day. The gas industry was also to blame, this gas man said, for not educating the public. If ignorance were dispelled, harmony would exist between company and customer.

The Massachusetts state inspector of gas and gas meters, Charles W. Hinman, was no friend of the newspaper jokes. "The utterance 'lies like a gas meter,'" he wrote, "is considered about the most forcible expression used for indicating want of veracity. My own experience has been much more favorable to the reliability of meters." In ten years 1,917 meters had been brought to him for reinspection. The average error was one-third of one per cent fast. In the last five years, gas being better purified, the average error of those fast and slow was even less. "A person frequently compares his gas bill with his neighbor's and finds it considerably larger," Inspector Hinman said, "but his neighbor's meter may be slow instead of his own being fast. It is probable the consumer gets better measurement of his gas than that of the average of his provisions and groceries."

Gas engineers in discussions among themselves took another approach. One said, observing "a very prevalent fashion to grumble at gas companies," that "if they improve their usefulness by improving the economy of kitchens and workshops, there will be much less cause or occasion." The engineers were considering the application of gas heat, its convenience and cleanliness versus coal, on the premise that some economical method of designing appliances could be found. As they figured, gas might come to be used to such an extent that daytime consumption would equal if

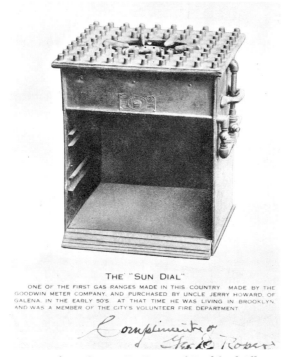

THE "SUN DIAL"

ONE OF THE FIRST GAS RANGES MADE IN THIS COUNTRY. MADE BY THE GOODWIN METER COMPANY, AND PURCHASED BY UNCLE JERRY HOWARD. OF GALENA. IN THE EARLY 50'S AT THAT TIME HE WAS LIVING IN BROOKLYN AND WAS A MEMBER OF THE CITY'S VOLUNTEER FIRE DEPARTMENT

Compliments of
George Roper

Memento from George D. Roper of Rockford, Illinois, who designed the "Eclipse" range in 1885

GAS STOVES.

THE introduction of Gas Stoves for cooking and heating purposes by many Gas Light Companies of the United States has been attended with good results, by increasing *the day* consumption of such Companies, and, as a natural result, correspondingly increasing their dividends. The introduction of Gas Stoves and Gas Engines is yet in its infancy; but it is, nevertheless, a very wide field for Gas Companies in which to operate, and with proper and judicious management on the part of the Companies is bound to be a source of profit to themselves and satisfactory to their consumers; as it has been clearly demonstrated that gas is the best, safest, cleanest,

Appliances introduced by meter manufacturers: *(upper left)* page from American Meter's 1880 Almanac; *(upper right)* page from McDonald's 1892 Annual; *(lower left)* Goodwin's "Sun Dial" 1884 model; *(lower right)* Metric Metal's "Classic," 1894

not exceed the night load. With service pipes already in, and daily production more uniform, the cost of manufacture and distribution should decline proportionately.

The idea of heating by gas had occurred to many minds and with impromptu effects. Crude articles that passed for stoves were advertised—a trivet, for example, to be set over a gaslight bracket. More ingenious were contraptions that adapted the Bunsen burner. This laboratory device, an upright tube with an air intake at the bottom, mixed air with gas before the point of burning and gave a blue, nonluminous flame of intense heat. It inspired bread toasters, oyster roasters, smoothing irons, and bathroom heaters. The first cooking stoves were imported from England and France; like them, American copies and modifications were rather short on efficiency.

Three years before the centennial exhibition publicized cooking with gas, the Providence (Rhode Island) Gas Light Company opened a gas appliance store. In that city the Retort Gas Stove Company was making stoves on the principle of "subheating the gas before it unites with the air" to avoid excessive consumption. The Retort, said advertisements, "Does not heat up the room or the person using it. The entire family cooking can be done in half the time and at half the cost of coal, wood, or oil." Other types were designed for parlor heating.

The American Meter Company took an agency for the Retort line in 1879 as an intermediary between the manufacturer and gas companies, hailing stoves as a means of "increasing *the day* consumption . . . and the rate of dividends."

> The introduction of Gas Stoves and Gas Engines is yet in its infancy; but it is, nevertheless, a very wide field for Gas Companies in which to operate. . . .
>
> Many companies are doing well in this direction; others have progressed but slowly. *These* we ask, where not in a position (as to locality, etc.) to introduce stoves to their customers, whether they will not interest themselves by calling on some reliable leading store or stores in their city or town to sell stoves, and name such houses to us. This we shall very fully appreciate.

In order to reach consumers in Philadelphia, the city of municipal gasworks, American Meter opened a stove store on Arch Street in 1879. The young man in charge asked about two years later to take the store off the company's hands, and he was given a line of credit. An examination of the stove accounts among the company customers showed this portion of the business was progressing satisfactorily. Those having limited facilities for retail selling could obtain samples and circulars to sell from. Soon American Meter was manufacturing its own brand of stoves in the Philadelphia factory, and reminding gas companies:

> The next point, and a *very important one*, is to select such stoves as will do *the largest* amount of good work with the *smallest* consumption of gas, otherwise the consumers will become dissatisfied, cease using the stoves, and speak disparagingly of them to their neighbors; whilst if using the most economical stove, and thereby getting the best possible results for amount of gas consumed, the result will be satisfaction, and the consumers themselves will be the best medium of advertising them.

The new line, called the Economy, was in full assortment for cooking and heating. Other items were gas furnaces for tinsmen's use, for solder and type-metal melting, apparatus for bending carriage panels, and water heaters for kitchen boilers and baths. Stoves for domestic use and in large sizes for restaurants and hotels "may be seen in operation at our retail store, No. 223 Sixth Avenue, New York."

This store originated in a proposal from the Manhattan Gas-Light Company in 1884 to pay the rent and furnish the gas if American Meter assumed the running expenses. The merchandise was to be "stoves and other articles as would tend to the further use of gas." The offer stemmed from the decision of a pool of six gas companies in the city to assess its members for the partial expense of three stores. Of the others, one was conducted by the Sheldon Gas Stove Company on West 22nd Street. The third, on West 14th Street, was under the wing of William W. Goodwin, now trading as The Goodwin Gas Stove and Meter Company and (so it seemed to other meter makers) scattering his energies.

Under this plan the gas companies agreed that consumers ordering stoves should not be charged for the pipe fittings. The

companies would absorb the cost up to five dollars in each case and bill the stove houses for any excess.

When the matter of continuing the Sixth Avenue store came up the next year, American Meter was again agreeable if the rent was paid, this time by Consolidated Gas Company of New York (the pool having solidified). But when the Chicago Gas Light and Coke Company asked American Meter to open and maintain a stove store in Chicago, the answer was no: experience so far in operating the New York store did not warrant embarking in like ventures elsewhere. On the other hand, the offer of the Cincinnati Gas Light Company to contribute toward the rent of the Cincinnati agency, if stoves besides those of American Meter's make were displayed, was accepted.

Gas companies in towns large and small took on the new role of selling stoves to sell more gas. The Consolidated arrangement went along from year to year. All this was missionary work, with elementary merchandising and elementary merchandise.

How the Cincinnati gas company induced consumers to visit the display was described at the first annual meeting of the Ohio Gas Light Association by General Andrew Hickenlooper, company president. He said testimonials to the merits of cooking with gas were printed on the backs of bills, six different housewives quoted each month. Stove sales were followed up by "a system similar to that practiced by sewing machine agents; that is, purchased a horse, harnessed it to a nice carriage, and employed a clever woman who was instructed to call at the residences of the ladies who had purchased stoves and inquire whether the cookers were performing satisfactorily." The trouble shooter made return calls as a Miss Fix-it.

A speaker from the town of Tiffin told the Ohio association meeting of having tried in vain to get hardware dealers to lay in a stock alongside their stoves for wood, coal, and oil. Next he sold direct from the company office, at net cost, and with increasing success and a better discount from the stove makers, at a small profit. The important thing, he said, was to select goods of proper size and working capacity, durable in material, tasteful in design. "My experience has led me to believe that the Economy is probably the most substantial stove, and the top burners are excellent, but I think the oven space is rather small. Housekeepers have often said to me, 'I like this stove, except that the oven is too

Station meter with 3000-cu. ft. drum capacity built by American Meter for Consolidated Gas Company of New York, (*Scientific American*, 1886)

small. I can only bake two pies at one time.' I then had some extra trays made in order to show that there was room enough for three pies.' "

Other Ohioans told of their gas-for-fuel crusades. "I loaded an express wagon with stoves," said a man from Delaware. "Went to the houses of our customers and requested the privilege of putting up a gas cooker. I said the stoves were not for sale—we only wanted a trial of these made. Our success was such that we did not have to take back half-a-dozen of the one hundred thirty-five so placed."

The gas company in Xenia rented an office, stocked it, and employed a woman who was a good cook. "She invited her lady friends to a lunch which was cooked on the gas stoves. Day after day she would thus entertain several parties. The women all went off pleased, talked to their husbands about the affair, and so got them interested. Every time she induced a masculine visitor to

Rival meter manufacturing companies, all of which later became constituents of American Meter under the presidency of John McIlhenny

partake of a lunch, prepared in front of him, a sale was almost sure to be effected."

The Columbus gas company president, P. W. Huntington, declared himself an old convert. "Speaking now as a consumer, for about five years every pound of food cooked in my house has been cooked on gas stoves. They save dirt, time, and *dollars*."

Stove manufacture in the United States was to advance with technology and specialization. For the season 1886 American Meter brought out larger sizes and, prompted by its agents, a new-style closed-top stove. But with American Meter, this branch of manufacturing was a sideline. Before long, offers to make stoves for its market were considered and orders were placed outside for its seasonal requirements. The trustees (directors) wavered and decided in 1893 to discontinue the line. The remaining stock of heating stoves at the factory and in the Sixth Avenue store was disposed of to the Bloomingdale Brothers department store for a special sale.

New kinds of meters for new kinds of consumers, and competition from a new generation of meter company managers, demanded concentrated attention.

Light from a natural gas well, near Pittsburgh, 1885

—3—

Beginnings of Natural Gas

THE NEEDS OF NATURAL GAS COMPANIES CAME BEFORE A BOARD MEETing of American Meter Company in the closing days of 1888. William N. Milsted, an officer for the past dozen years and latterly general superintendent, was authorized to look into the matter of cast-iron cases. For a long time there had been a general assumption that natural gas could not be measured for consumers. Satisfactory regulators for reducing the high pressure of gas wells were unavailable. The tincase meters developed for manufactured gas were considered unsuitable in the belief that high-pressure gas entering them would give false readings, if not fracture the meters.

Within a year Milsted, who had an inventive turn (he held patents on meters, stoves, and water heaters), was ready with an ironcase dry meter designed for high-pressure use. Moreover, he obtained a trial order for one hundred from Joseph N. Pew, the head of Peoples Natural Gas Company of Pittsburgh, of a size to be called "300 feet per hour."

At this time natural-gas transmission and distribution was beginning to be a commercial success after romantic, accidental, and uninhibited origins.

Nature's hidden resource revealed itself in seepages and springs here and there before an historic event took place in Fredonia, New York, in 1821. Flame seen on Canadaway Creek, at this village near Lake Erie, inspired a gunsmith to dig a well. He drilled bores through logs and piped gas to an inn across the road and to nearby houses. When General Lafayette revisited the United States a few years later, he stopped at Fredonia to marvel at the inn and streets lighted by gas from the earth.

From the Kanawha Valley of West Virginia to the western flank of the Appalachians in Pennsylvania and over the state line in

New York came subsequent news of natural gas. Wells dug for brine revealed gas, and this was piped to saltworks to heat evaporating pans. Other flows were used locally for light and fuel until exhausted. In the hectic search for oil after the lucky strike near Titusville, Pennsylvania, in 1859, gas frequently was found as an oil vapor overhanging a pool. Little notice was taken of a report of gas discovered in Kansas. It was Pennsylvania that had nature's plenitude.

In the city of Erie natural gas was taken into the mains in 1870 from wells drilled around town. In Titusville it entered homes in 1872 via a two-inch iron pipeline five miles long. Joseph Pew helped organize a company in Bradford in 1881 which obtained a franchise to supply the village of Olean, New York.

For the most part, natural gas was used for industrial purposes—heating furnaces of iron, pottery, and glass works. George Westinghouse found gas on his property outside Pittsburgh and formed a gas company to serve mills and houses in that city (1884). Andrew Carnegie was so enthusiastic about natural gas, he declared it would save 10,000 tons of coal a day.

Abundant flows appeared next in northern Ohio and next-door Indiana. Gas wells became passports to prosperity for many a town. There was so much gas, so cheap, it seemed unnecessary to charge for it by the thousand feet. On a flat rate consumers took all they wanted, all they wanted to squander, using wasteful burners, leaving fires and lights on night and day, having no incentive to economize. Gas history was repeating itself. Hastily undertaken companies got into trouble and did not get out of it even after varying rates according to appliances used. Worse, from a national standpoint, profligate consumption shortened the life of many a gas field.

In Pittsburgh, Westinghouse put consumers on meters of his own design. As other companies realized that supplies were not limitless, they awoke to the necessity of station meters and consumer meters. This changed outlook put the business on a profitable footing, with homes and factories paying their proportionate share for gas and service received. It was estimated that meters saved more than 60 per cent in the quantity consumed. Meters also made it possible to test piping for leaks of this odorless gas, for by turning off all fires and lights one could note by the small dial whether any gas was passing.

Long-distance transmission was developed in a copy of oil pipelines. Buffalo, New York, received gas from McKean County, Pennsylvania, more than 87 miles away (1886); Detroit was on a 92-mile line from Ohio fields near Findlay (1889) and Chicago on two parallel lines of eight-inch wrought-iron pipe laid 120 miles from Greentown, Indiana (1891). The gas sent to Chicago was principally for fuel, not being considered good enough for illumination, and sold for fifty cents per thousand cubic feet. (Pressure from the Indiana wells soon declined, along with exhaustion of half the natural gas in the state, and the dual line to Chicago was abandoned after a few years.) Transmission methods improved. A short pipeline laid down by Solomon R. Dresser, of Bradford, to demonstrate his flexible couplings, convinced natural-gas engineers that such pipes could be joined tightly and securely.

By 1891 natural gas was being distributed in at least a dozen states, and the companies were generally resolved on dropping the consumer-contract basis. In Pittsburgh, where gas had been delivered without restriction at fifteen cents a month for lights and a dollar a month for cooking ranges, the price of metered gas was fourteen cents per thousand. The cylindrical, cast-iron meters that American Meter furnished Joseph Pew and others on repeat

Main Street of Findlay, Ohio, 1885, lighted by local natural gas

Calvin N. Payne   The first meter made
                                   for natural gas, 1888

orders were capable of passing gas to seven fires. They bore indexes recording up to a million feet.

The honor of precedence in making ironcase, high-pressure meters belonged to a company started in 1888 at Beaver Falls, Pennsylvania, and financed largely by persons in Pittsburgh associated with Standard Oil. Their leading man was Calvin N. Payne, an associate of John D. Rockefeller in charge of Standard's natural-gas interests. He had reached this rank in a career that began in Erie as a conductor on the Philadelphia & Erie Railroad; after hieing off to Petroleum Center he was successively a teamster hauling barrels of oil, a driller, and an independent oil operator. The new firm, organized to supply "the fuel gas trade," was called Metric Metal Company. It owned patents on a circular meter with a single round diaphragm and a case capable of withstanding pressures up to thirty pounds to the square inch. Shipments went out by the thousand to Standard's outlets in Sandusky, Toledo, and Clyde, Ohio, and Detroit.

Before a year was out, Metric Metal's directors were considering a proposal to combine with "the Westinghouse people." They were willing to sell for $100,000 cash and 20 per cent of the Westinghouse stock. The deal fell through.

Soon Metric Metal needed an additional plant to duplicate its production facilities. Buffalo, Cleveland, and Erie were consid-

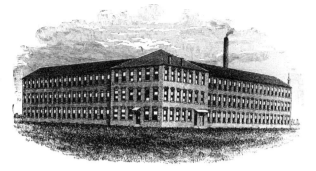

Advertisement in 1894, before Metric Metal became a unit
of American Meter; Tobey shown in lower right corner

Tobey meter, showing diaphragm,
base, valve seat, and other parts

American Meter's ironcase for
measuring natural gas, 1891

ered as likely locations. Calvin Payne, who kept an office in Oil City, went up to Erie, his wife's home town, the scene of iron foundries and old memories. There he bought thirty acres at $400 an acre. The city council agreed to open up Tenth Street and let the railroad lay switch tracks along it to the proposed factory site.

In the summer of 1891 construction of a large, three-story plant was started on the corner of Tenth Street and a road to be designated as Payne Avenue. Payne's twenty-three-year-old son, Francis H., just graduated from Princeton, was elected secretary-treasurer. In October, machinery was transferred from the works at Beaver Falls and Frank Payne became manager, starting a fifty-year reign.

Metric Metal announced its reason for a building with excess capacity: a belief in the future of gas, in greater annual consumption, "and this not through the wasteful contract system, but with the use of meters."

> Every day we find some Natural Gas Company awakening to the fact that unless consumption be regulated, their gas lands will soon cease to yield. With a meter in the house, the consumer is driven to using economical burning appliances, while the Distributor can realize at once that he has found a means to store up for future use this grandest fuel known to man.

Stoves and fireplace burners supplemented the Erie output, and a new meter superseded the original hardcase as a result of a contract negotiated by Calvin Payne, president, in December. A Toledo inventor named Henry A. Tobey, who held patents on steam traps, a steam engine, and a water-closet valve, had approached him with a spherical device. It was flat at top and bottom and encased three diaphragms with a three-port rotary valve seat at the base. The Tobey cast-iron meter could stand a pressure of ninety pounds. Metric Metal put it into immediate production in four sizes, the largest capable of 1500 cubic feet per hour.

This meter firm's belief in the future of gas was not confined to fuel use despite the formation of many Edison companies and the presence of electric arc lights on some of Erie's streets. "For the illuminating gas trade we have added a large tin meter department. . . . We make the tin meter after the old established pattern, having improved materially many parts of construction. . . . We claim that our meters will run more accurately and stand the strain longer than any other meter manufactured."

D. McDonald & Company was a bit more restrained. In the same year (1892) this Albany house with a fine reputation for tincase meters spoke of engaging in making meters particularly for natural gas, saying, "After five years of experience in this *special* line we believe we can guarantee for our meters."

Rivalry posed no obstacle to cooperation among the meter houses when the needs of the American Gas Light Association were involved. A committee appointed by the association to work up standards for uniform meter couplings consisted of William H. Down (son of the late Samuel Down and secretary of American Meter) as chairman; William W. Goodwin, as secretary; and John J. Griffin, Nathaniel Tufts, William Helme, and William McDonald (associated since 1860 with his father, Donald McDonald, now retired). Their unanimous agreement on meter unions prompted John P. Harbison, of the Hartford (Connecticut) Gas Light Company, to rise in meeting to remark,

> Their interests are ours and ours theirs. I like to see this friendly feeling existing among them and to know that they have agreed to make such changes as are necessary and to go to such expense as is required and to so manage their business as best suits the wishes of their customers.

In competition for gas company orders, of course, there was no let-up. The whole United States was everybody's oyster. McDonald enjoyed good trade in Tufts' Boston, although Tufts had most of the New England business and did a large repair operation for the many neighboring small-town companies, which had no repair shops. Maryland Meter & Manufacturing Company (new name of Dickey, Tansley) formed agencies in San Francisco and Los Angeles, and American Meter instructed its Coast representative to meet Maryland's prices. American Meter did not get all, but a majority, of the business placed by Consolidated Gas in New York. The several Philadelphia firms competed locally and nationally.

There was the time the Philadelphia Gas Works invited bids

for a station meter, and Goodwin underbid Harris, Griffin & Company and American Meter. A fortnight before, a similar Philadelphia contract had been awarded to Helme & McIlhenny. Station meters were getting bigger and bigger to meet the gas companies' growing needs. American Meter, installing them from Yarmouth, Nova Scotia, to Seattle, Washington Territory, erected one 11 feet high for the Nassau Gas-Light Company (Brooklyn) and then capped this with a thirteen-footer for the Brooklyn Gas-Light Company. In 1892 American Meter built and shipped by vessel to San Francisco two drums for station meters sixteen and a half feet in diameter.

Harris, Helme & McIlhenny had been abbreviated to Helme & McIlhenny when the last of the Harrises withdrew in 1885 and William E. Helme became a partner of his father and John McIlhenny. Harris, Griffin & Company dissolved in 1890 and was succeeded by John J. Griffin & Company, with son-in-law John Gribbel as junior partner managing the New York end. Charles E. Dickey's son, Charles H., acquired an interest in Maryland Meter and astutely engaged a New Englander, Harry A. Norton, as salesman in Boston to contend with Tufts. The second generation was steaming ahead.

Publication of pocket manuals and almanacs for gas superintendents and engineers was a means employed by large meter

A Boston source of tincase meters, apparatus for New England utility companies, and repair service

Maryland Meter's factory on the site of the original Baltimore gasworks

makers in vying for good will. Each year new editions were issued with tables giving the time for lighting and extinguishing public lamps according to sunset and sunrise and phases of the moon. (In some localities the lamplighter was not required to make his rounds when the moon was full.) The technical data and rules in these handsome, leather-bound annuals made them handy reference books.

Other opportunities for help presented themselves when meter manufacturers were asked to draw on their specialized knowledge for talks before gas associations. They were active members of the American Gas Light Association and regional groups.

Age took its toll; familiar faces departed: Nathaniel Tufts died in 1890, William Down the following year, and in one sweep, Donald McDonald, the elder William Helme, and John J. Griffin died in 1892. William Goodwin was ailing and inactive.

In management changes that took place, Tufts was being run by Charles W. Hinman, the former Massachusetts inspector (who, incidentally, was developing a new kind of station meter drum). The current president of American Meter, who took office after Thomas Hopper's resignation, was George J. McGourkey, executor of the Down estate (Milsted stood next in line). The Griffin firm, flourishing in a recently built factory on Race Street, was in the forceful hands of Gribbel.

The meter business as a whole went well. Signs of the times

were expansions in addition to Griffin's. American Meter took over a building in the rear of its New York factory to keep up with orders from Consolidated Gas, and Maryland Meter acquired corner property (the original location of the Baltimore gas house) between its plant on North Street and its overcrowded warehouse on Saratoga Street. Unforeseen, a national panic was imminent.

The depression that saddled the country in 1893 was variously attributed to the hoarding of gold, uneasiness about silver, the second election of President Grover Cleveland, and curtailment of manufacturing through fear of unfavorable legislation. Credit was stringent. Meter houses, no exception, went on short work-weeks and strained after loans. In the minute book of Metric Metal's board of directors was a tell-tale note: "Much anxiety was expressed as to how long the present dullness would last and as to what plan was best to cope with the situation." Calvin Payne saved this company by personally endorsing and guaranteeing its notes.

During the year, officers of five meter houses, styling themselves "Parties in Interest," met in Philadelphia to join in an informal association similar to one in England. John McIlhenny, dean of the trade, was chairman. Some of the men had authorization to press for a more definite arrangement. Payne, attending a later session, declined membership on the ground that Metric Metal should not be bound by dubious agreements while trying to build up its business. Maryland Meter was an abstainee. The others urged Payne to submit his ideas on a plan for a closer union. This he did without delay, proposing a consolidation of all meter manufacturers. The "Parties in Interest" replied with a rejection.

Calvin Payne was not deterred. The vogue for consolidations pervaded American industry, even as necessity forced them on gas companies in numerous cities. He pursued his purpose with the five association members individually and at last won an adherent, John Gribbel. Through 1894 no further progress was made. The separate parties were working in their own interest.

Meanwhile, Metric Metal proceeded to promote an extra-heavy tincase meter for natural gas, which gave "excellent results where the line pressure is controlled." The people in Erie also ventured tentatively into the manufacture of cooking stoves with a patented self-lighter and double-cock, but met with disappointment as flaws in construction showed up. The ironcase Tobeys, however, were going strong, finding additional welcome where houses without cellars required placing meters in locations exposed to the weather.

The latest thing in meters in 1894 were attachments that made them "coin-freed." American manufacturers, observing English experience with these devices, and encouraged by customers, entered the new area.

First intimation had come in a report in *The American Gas-Light Journal* in 1888:

> An ingenious inventor, by name Mr. R. W. Brownhills of Birmingham, has just introduced an automatic gas meter, based on the principle of the machines used for the automatic sale of cigarettes, chocolate, etc. This meter will not pass gas until it has been propitiated by the insertion of one penny in a slot provided for that purpose. It then delivers gas until the equivalent in value of the coin has passed through, and as this quantity is approached the light begins to diminish and will eventually go out, unless the meter is refreshed by the supply of a second coin. The idea is to facilitate the use of gas amongst the poorer classes, by enabling them to pay as they go on. . . .
>
> Several models of the automatic meter have been shown in public, and they work efficiently. There is something pleasant about the idea of securing the money beforehand. . . .

Various English makes were in service within a few years in large cities, notably Liverpool, and at cottages in small rural towns. Gas companies that set them spoke of "our latest friends, the coin meter consumers." Alert American manufacturers acquired rights under the British patents. President Milsted of American Meter went abroad in the fall of 1893 and came back with an agreement with Wm. Parkinson & Company fixing a royalty of one shilling for each Carter Patent Coin-Freed Gas Meter his firm made and sold. Next, Milsted visited Consolidated Gas and found its officers "much pleased with the action taken in regard to prepayment meters." He got a standing order for one thousand a year.

Prepayment meters, as they were now called, made their debut

Early prepayment meters;
(*above*) Griffin's attachment
for nickels

The Glover Prepayment Meter

MADE FOR 25 CENT PIECES ONLY.

SOLE MAKERS AND LICENSEES IN THE UNITED STATES:

D. McDONALD & CO.,

51, 53 and 55 Lancaster Street.   Albany, N. Y.

in the United States early in 1894. Griffin brought out a model of
Sawyer & Purves design with the mechanism superimposed and
a slot for nickels (forty cubic feet for five cents, for example).
Helme & McIlhenny's, like most others, had a coin cylinder and
handle secured to the left side of the meter. All makes operated
more or less on the same principle, though some were more complicated and troublesome than others. The coin (usually a quarter) opened the valve and, as gas passed, a price wheel with
teeth or holes (each having a specific value) began revolving.
A credit dial indicated the number of feet paid for and not yet used,
and on a full turn of the wheel the registration and gas supply
stopped. Additional coins could be deposited beforehand to keep
the home fires burning. For a lower or higher price, a wheel with
fewer or more teeth was easily substituted.

Consolidated Gas notified American Meter in the spring of
1894 that they wanted much greater quantities of the Parkinson
meter and exclusive right to it in New York City; they also
expected American Meter to increase manufacturing facilities
accordingly. Parkinson, in turn, offered to rebate royalties for the
year if American guaranteed to use no patent but theirs. Regarding the latter proposal, American Meter's board preferred to

John McIlhenny   William E. Helme   William McDonald

retain freedom of action. Besides, Milsted now held a prepayment
meter patent.

"To increase the business of the Gas Company is the direct
concern of the meter maker," said McDonald, meeting the competition with a license for the Glover Prepayment Meter. This
make had a simplified cartwheel mechanism on the side, for
twenty-five-cent pieces only. It was "perfect in mechanical detail,"
and McDonald did not hesitate to call the Glover the best on the
market. "In facilitating the introduction of stoves" to non-con-
sumers and people who dreaded bills, "it cannot be equalled, and
we need not dwell on the advantage of an increase in the day
consumption." No need to dwell—because the gas industry was
well aware of the incandescent electric light's invasion of its
nights.

The year 1895 was still young when the five firms in the meter
makers' association—"organized for the mutual benefit of its members and the extension of sociability"—all acknowledged the logic
of Calvin Payne's idea of consolidation. They negotiated with
him and among themselves and signed a preliminary agreement.
In April, Gribbel was received at the annual meeting of American
Meter stockholders for a recital of plans to merge Griffin, McDonald, Helme & McIlhenny, Goodwin, and Metric Metal with their
company. Each firm was to turn over its property after appraisal

Charles H. Dickey, as general manager of Maryland Meter

for 6 per cent debentures and be given stock in the ratio of its average net earnings for 1892-94 to the combined earnings.

As each plant's inventory was completed, the firm entered the combination: Metric Metal on July 1, all six by July 31. The inventories totaled close to $650,000.

When it came to the division of stock according to proportionate earnings, Calvin Payne again asserted strength of mind. Accountants presented a combined figure of $214,000 as an average year, representing 10 per cent on $2,140,000, but to be on the safe side it was decided to issue only $2,000,000 of stock. Payne refused to accept the accountants' report of $13,000 as Metric Metal's portion, declaring that the base years were not fair in this instance, since his company was just getting off the ground. He persuaded several of the others to yield a little on their figures and managed to bring Metric's up to $20,000. On the revised basis the stock was divided, Metric getting 20/214 instead of 13/214 of the $2,000,000 issued.

In November 1895 the properties, excluding real estate, were conveyed to American Meter. John McIlhenny was elected president, Milsted having resigned in his favor and becoming secretary. Gribbel was elected vice president, William E. Helme treasurer. The post of general superintendent of all factories was given to William McDonald, who continued as manager in Albany, while Gribbel was manager at Race Street, McIlhenny's son John D. at Cherry Street, Henry R. Cartwright at Arch Street, and Frank Payne in Erie. The Goodwin plant was to be closed.

Most of the factory buildings were owned by estates, which declined to sell but agreed to rent. Metric Metal Company put in its plant on six acres and accepted cash and notes. Calvin Payne dropped out of the picture, but not without a vote of thanks from fellow stockholders for his help in the panic of 1893, his five years' service as president without pay, and "the advantageous sale of our property." With the thanks went $10,000 of American Meter stock in Metric's treasury before distribution. (McGourkey, in the same spirit of self-dedication, had filled the American Meter presidency at $100 a year, at his own request, when the regular salary attached to that office was $1500.)

The consolidated concern began functioning on January 1, 1896. After an increase in capitalization to $3,000,000, Maryland Meter came into the fold and other acquisitions were in prospect. Charles H. Dickey assumed the title of general manager in Baltimore, with his younger brother Edmund at his elbow as man-

Francis H. Payne in his Erie office, 1895

ager. In view of his influence in Boston, C.H. was appointed to a committee to go there "with power to act in making arrangements as they deem beneficial to the Company's interests."

The quarry in Boston was Tufts. The biggest asset, Harry Norton. With a background of gas company affiliation in Nashua, New Hampshire, and a gift for verbalizing his convictions, Norton had won a host of friends for the Maryland line. Neither the small Tufts company nor C. W. Hinman & Company (formed by Charles Hinman to manufacture station meters and specialties he designed) fared well in the face of Norton's success. A sequel to the Dickey committee's visit was the purchase of Nathaniel Tufts Meter Company, with Norton becoming the manager. In another sequel, Hinman was bought and closed out, the property turned over to Tufts.

All the constituent companies kept the names by which they had built up followings in the industry, except that Erie did business as Metric Metal Works (1897) and Baltimore eventually shortened its title to Maryland Meter Company (1902). A way of life evolved as to interrelations. Rules were established for inter-plant sales, on the source of prepayment meter locks, on contracting for tinplate supplies and placing of advertising, and assessment of contributions to educational work of the American Gas Light Association. The seasoned wisdom and sunny optimism of President McIlhenny harmonized the personalities of individualists accustomed to independence. His long regime did not dissolve personal pride nor melt competitive fervor, but rather welded the organization into a firm ally of the gas companies in meeting a challenge to survival.

—4—

Increasing the Daytime Load

THE GREAT WHITE WAY—FOR PEOPLE FAMILIAR WITH GAS HISTORY, this phrase acquired a discordant ring. No longer did it evoke the innovation of gas street lamps replacing oil lamps on New York's lower Broadway. Someone crowing over electricity, perhaps thinking he was coining the expression, thus dramatized the array of arc lights strung along Broadway from Union Square to Madison Square in 1881. Science was on the march. It might overtake gas.

The demonstration of electric lamps on ornate posts did indeed soon move the city administration to give the Brush Electric Illuminating Company and the United States Illuminating Company contracts for some of the thoroughfares and parks. In Philadelphia similar glass balls of white light began shining on streets. By the mid-1880s in Baltimore the number of street lamps was declining, brilliant electric arc lights taking the place of gas at the rate of two for five.

Gas managers in these cities and many towns stood by as electric companies encroached on the business of outdoor lighting. They were not altogether disheartened, for public lamps in general accounted for only a tenth of the gas consumed, a not very profitable segment at that. But the new entrepreneurs in their midst were not limiting themselves.

When Charles F. Brush presented his arc light, one of his first installations was in a Philadelphia store, John Wanamaker's. When it arrived in Baltimore it gleamed in the window of another clothing store. Thomas A. Edison, whose incandescent lamp with a filament of carbonized bamboo was startling the world, had given himself a major project. In his notebook he had written, "Edison to effect exact imitation of all done by gas, so as to replace lighting by gas, by lighting by electricity."

Plenty of gaslight in the dressing room of John D. Rockefeller's mansion in New York, 1884

Edison's central station for generating and distributing electricity in New York started out with nearly sixty stores and houses on the circuit, making a total of four hundred lamps supplied at low voltage. Patronage increased, but the direct current of the "jumbo" dynamo could reach no further than a mile. Time and the persistence of George Westinghouse were to break the distance barrier with alternating current. Meanwhile, Edison companies popped up in far-flung communities, their equipment crude and the "light of the future" sometimes a light that failed. Wires entwined around household gas fixtures looked like parasitic vines to the gas man. In homes that were wired, many a former gas customer demanded that the gas meter remain as an insurance against electricity failure. Among large gas consumers there were threats of wiring if they did not get quantity discounts.

The lighting load represented about 95 per cent of most gas companies' output. It was not going to be surrendered without a struggle. Socrates Newman of the St. Louis Gas Light Company heard of a new gas lamp, a cluster of four burners producing 150 candlepower, recently placed in front of the Houses of Parliament. He sent to London for some. The *St. Louis Republican* carried the story with these headlines:

SUGG'S LAMP
A Prediction that It will Put an End
to the Electric Light Furor

American Meter Company obtained patent rights to the Sugg lamp and arranged for its manufacture. The market proved quite limited.

Thaddeus Lowe sought an incandescent gaslight that would give a steadier, brighter glow than the yellow open flame of the common fishtail or flat burner. In theaters it had been customary to heat a piece of limestone in a flame for stage lighting and projection. The refractory material Lowe used was a spiral of platinum fitted into an ordinary slit-tip burner. He repeated the experiment in an exhibition of the Franklin Institute in Philadelphia and won acclaim. The effect was luminous, but not of high candlepower, and it required gas at exceptional pressure.

What held promise as an article competitive to the electric lamp was an incandescent gas mantle invented by Professor Robert von Bunsen's pupil, Carl Auer (von Welsbach), in his chemical laboratory at Heidelberg. The Welsbach mantle resulted from Auer's need for a continuous light in spectrographic studies. He utilized the heating power of gas. Making a hood of finely woven long-staple cotton, he saturated it in rare earth oxides and ignited it, getting a fragile skeleton of the impregnated materials. By suspending this mantle over an upright Bunsen burner, Auer not only achieved illumination without a flame but more than doubled the candlepower of an open flame with half the usual amount of gas (1885).

Skepticism greeted the claims. A less patronizing attitude followed an exhibit of Welsbach mantles in a Pall Mall art gallery, where the lights brought out all the shades of green and blue in the paintings on the walls. The United Gas Improvement Company formed a subsidiary, the Welsbach Incandescent Light Company, to manufacture the mantles. Erstwhile critics now saw the possibility of using cheap fuel-gas for lighting instead of oil-enriched illuminating gas, hence a single quality for all purposes at a low price.

Consumers took to the Welsbach mantle slowly. Habit was one factor. Disinclination to spend extra money was another. Also, the mantles crumbled if mishandled, blackened if jarred. The inventor worked on improvements and hit on the right combination of the right rare earths. The product of the early 1890's gave three times as much illumination as old-style burners with half the gas, and a careful calculation showed what a good buy was gas. On the basis of $1.25 per thousand cubic feet, and electricity at twenty cents a kilowatt hour, one hundred candlepower would cost less than a cent an hour via Welsbach mantles as against six cents with electric lamps.

It was the enemy's turn to get jittery. *Electrical Engineering* figured that gas companies were able to sell more cheaply because they got 74 per cent more light from a pound of coal than the electric companies with their present machines and bulbs. The trade journal asked, "How can electric light companies meet this competition?"

As the Welsbach mantle became commercially successful, simultaneously with the growing popularity of electric lights among people eager to go modern, its historical function was a delaying action. It prolonged the period of the gas companies' loss of the illuminating business. It postponed the wiring of many houses. Gas street lamps lingered. Stores used large-size mantles. An inverted Welsbach, introduced later, eliminated shadow, and the downwardly directed gas developed higher heat inside the hood for double the candlepower. Electrical technology was also advancing, but the interim afforded the gas industry a chance to seek salvation in cooking and other heating applications.

Probably the low efficiency of stoves heretofore and a fear of high bills had held the transformation of the kitchen to a slow pace; or the fault may have been inept promotion. Certainly meter makers had made an effort, going outside their regular lines—Maryland among others with its Success ranges, McDonald with Star ranges and with Square parlor heaters for further gas consumption. The record showed that the gas companies had made sporadic attempts to foster cooking. Now they had incentive to be more aggressive.

"The time has passed for gas companies to sell their product for illuminating purposes only," an Ohio superintendent reminded fellow members of his association. "To introduce gas as a fuel the

Robert W. von Bunsen

Left:
Open-flame burner   Carl Auer von Welsbach
Right:
Incandescent burner

companies must proceed in an energetic and practical manner, and it can only be done where they are willing to sell gas for the lowest figure commensurate with a little profit. The summer consumption of many consumers can thus be made to overrun the winter use of gas."

Some companies had tried fixing a flat yearly rate per stove of family size, a higher one for hotel and large-size ranges. Others reduced their price if the customer put in a stove, then found, as this Ohioan did, quite a few people imposing on them by not using the gas for fuel. "I told the consumers that if they wanted cheap gas they must increase their use of it so that we could afford to sell at low rates." A sliding scale of discounts was the answer.

There was also a job of education to do. Servants were in the habit of leaving fires burning all day, as was their wont with coal stoves. They were not entirely blameworthy, since coal stoves often furnished hot water; but separate gas water-heaters were obtainable.

Great help came from new appliance manufacturers. They were not content with improving the appearance of cast-iron stoves with nickel plating and decorative motifs. They put their minds on mechanical design for more satisfactory performance. By producing more salable merchandise in the 1890s, they sped up acceptance of cooking with gas.

Inventors filled another breach with automatic water heaters. H. A. Tobey started the series with thermostatic control of gas flow. A copper heating coil and a water-pressure valve for control were the next contributions. Edwin Ruud combined the two controls. A Pittsburgher named F. W. Robertshaw solved his personal problem of having to run up and down cellar stairs for the family's hot-water needs by inventing a rod-and-tube thermostat.

Although water heaters and other appliances were marketed, including gas-fired irons and bread toasters, gas companies concentrated their promotional zeal on cooking. Sometimes they gave a minor assist to advocates of "domestic science," as when the Boston Cooking School held lecture classes at a hotel in Vincennes, Indiana (separate courses for housewives, young ladies, and servants), the Citizens Gas Light Company lent a range and furnished the gas. Mostly, the aroused companies took the initiative.

A case in point was the program of The Peoples Gas-Light and Coke Company in Chicago. Service lines were run into vacant lots and people were invited to bring food they wanted cooked and see for themselves how easily meals could be prepared on ranges. One salesman in 1898 loaded a range on a horse-drawn wagon and carried his message to folks' front doors by connecting rubber hose to a street lamppost. That year the company sold 20,343 stoves.

The American Gas Light Association took notice of "new business" accomplishments of a company in Madison, Wisconsin, by inviting its manager, Henry L. Doherty, to talk on the topic, "How Can We Make the Use of Gas for Cooking More Universal?" A special significance was attached to the speaker—his firm was called Madison Gas and Electric Company.

A fact of industrial life was that gas and electric interests were tending to merge. In Erie, the majority of the shares of the Erie Gas Company passed into the hands of a consolidated electric concern; in some other cities, gas companies absorbed price-war-worn electric companies. Either way, the meaning was clear. The field was divided. Cooking and heating were conceded to gas.

The Columbian Exposition in Chicago in 1893 had marked the peak of the gaslight era. No future world's fair would see parkways and buildings flooded with gas illumination as this was.

Despite the entrenchment of electricity, and because time had been won for gas to develop other applications, gas consumption steadily increased. The nation in the 1890s was expanding as never before, giving room for growth to every public service. Gas companies found it necessary to provide themselves with larger facilities for production. And they needed new station meters to measure the output.

Before storing gas in a holder, a check had to be made on the amount produced per ton or pound of coal and on labor and other costs. The measurement must be positive, not approximate. Experience to date demonstrated that gas in large quantities could be measured accurately and continuously only by a wet meter which did it by displacement. The wet station meter registered a cubic foot for each actual cubic foot of gas passed, no matter what conditions of temperature or pressure prevailed within.

No change had been made in wet meter construction since its adoption except for a slight modification of the drum: three partitions instead of four. As the need arose for greater capacity, attempts were made to gain it by decreasing the size of the drum's core or center opening. Charles Hinman had a revolutionary idea, literally. He determined that greater capacity could be obtained by safe increase in the speed of drum revolution. The partitions were the key. He reverted to four. He slanted them at different angles, gave an extra pitch to each end-section, and in other ways lessened resistance to the water seal and permitted freer movement of gas. Patented in 1896, the Hinman drum was destined to be the standard.

Hinman transferred his rights in station meter patents to American Meter Company for a percentage of the selling price of station meters built with his drums and of the price received for drums built for repairs. The Tufts unit of the company gave up drums of English make to switch to the new type. The McDonald unit in Albany, however, being quite active in station meters and loath to cede its New England customers, was the first American Meter factory to build with Hinman drums. Helme & McIlhenny was also authorized.

These cylindrical station meters, usually in cast-iron cases, were shipped complete, ready to set up and run, in sizes up to eight feet. Larger sizes, some of wrought iron, were shipped in sections and built on location. Before delivery the meters were tested for detection of leaks and proved, with exact water-line established, to hold a given amount per revolution, the index geared to register correctly. Tests were made with a wet test meter, which itself was proved to be correct at a given rate of speed.

The economy and accuracy of the new station meters attracted demands from Montreal to Havana and points west. Unprecedented sizes were called for, so big that buildings had to be erected around them. Some were ordered in pairs; other installations consisted of five. Two for the 21st Street station of Consolidated Gas Company of New York were eighteen and a half feet in diameter and length, each weighing sixty-four tons and containing sixty-four tons of water. Four, measuring seventeen by seventeen feet, were installed at the Harrison, New Jersey, station of the Public Service Electric & Gas Company. A McDonald benchman, Charles Bollinger, and his assistant, James J. Cooney, afterward became familiar constructors at gasworks over

Maryland Meter delivery wagon ready for loading, 1902

Meter setters in Atlanta, about 1906

the country. Among the achievements of their long careers were sixteen station meters for the Astoria (Long Island, New York) Light, Heat and Power Company.

The surge in gas consumption meant more consumer meters, and American Meter needed larger factories in which to make them. A story added to McDonald's Lancaster Street plant in Albany in 1898 soon proved insufficient; a plot on Broadway at Tivoli Street was acquired for a brand-new building. Griffin, selected for expansion in Philadelphia, also got another story in 1899. Fire destroyed this factory a few years later; American Meter bought the site from John Gribbel and rebuilt. Thus another factory came under direct ownership, the list already including Maryland Meter and Tufts. Land was cleared on Commercial Street, Boston, along the Charles River, for a modern six-story Tufts plant, to be gas-heated from the start. The New York premises, spacious but outmoded after half a century, also had to leave its past behind. A six-story building went up at 11th Avenue and 47th Street in 1900.

Metric Metal Works spread out on its acreage in Erie, first with a brass foundry, 1898, next with a building for white metal

Derbies were in style for Chicago meter men

casting and a warehouse addition, later with a three-story extension to the main structure. As a concession to modernity, the American Meter directors authorized the general superintendent to provide an electric lighting plant for this factory.

Full-scale local manufacturing became essential for the growing area served by the Chicago branch. Property was bought ·at Monroe and Jefferson Streets in 1900 and a three-story factory erected for finishing and repairing. Carl Asendorf, who had been managing the office, was appointed superintendent.

For better development of the market in Canada, instead of shipping from the recently acquired Detroit Meter Company, a shop was set up in Windsor, Ontario, in 1900 under the name of The Canadian Meter Company, Ltd. William McDonald was the titular head. John B. McNary, originally from the Albany factory, went over to manage the Windsor works, using a waterwheel for power. Here tincase meters were made for natural-gas companies in southwestern Ontario and for manufactured gas elsewhere. Tobeys from Erie were supplied for roadside settings in farm districts. Albany sent station meter parts.

Encouraged by the reception of its service, the Canadian company moved on to Hamilton, Ontario, to be closer to Toronto's larger sales potential. The factory built in 1905 was in fact centrally located, Montreal being accessible. McNary grew in stature with the people of the Dominion industry; he was associated with the founders of The Canadian Gas Association and accepted into its membership during its first year, 1907, and in time served as the association's president.

Back at the turn of the century American Meter had taken another geographical step. This was the formation of the Pacific Meter Company in San Francisco in 1901, William McDonald collecting one more title as president. American Meter and Maryland Meter stocks in the Coast agent's hands were transferred to a loft on Fremont Street, and arrangements were made to supply Pacific Meter with merchandise of the associated companies for the Far Western and Japanese trade. In another transaction the new firm received the privilege of selling prepayment meters manufactured by Griffin, McDonald, and Helme & McIlhenny.

Said John McIlhenny in an annual report to American Meter stockholders:

It seems to be a settled conviction of the people who are managing and who own gasworks property that the gas business will keep on increasing with the growth of the cities and towns.

The writer well remembers several scares that lessened the confidence of the public in the permanence of the gas business and reduced the value of all such property, and our business also was injuriously affected. It was predicted that the electric light would eclipse us and drive us out. . . . [But prosperity surmounted gloomy prophecies.] Gas is steadily becoming more and more the light and fuel of the masses. It is also constantly being reduced in price. This is the strength of the meter business. . . . As the meter business necessarily grows with the gas business, we are tempted to be confident of the future.

There was also the matter of growing pains. Consumption taxed the capacity of consumer meters. Something had to be done to enable them to deliver more gas.

—5—

New Developments in Meters

HAVING TAKEN ON HEATING LOADS, THE GAS COMPANIES REQUIRED much more efficiency of a meter than when the only load was lighting. Gas ranges with oven controls, gas water-heaters, radiators, radiant fires, and small space-heating units had emerged from the Gay Nineties to become established household fixtures in the twentieth century. They were the stock in trade of department stores, furniture stores, and plumbers. Although professional opinion was not yet settled as to the proper mechanics of house heating by gas, this demand existed too.

It would have been easy to meet greater service requirements with meters of larger size—at a waste of capital investment. Meters comprised an impressive part of the capital account of every gas company. A superintendent of distribution had to make practical and economical installations, suiting each to the particular need. Many families ordinarily used a small quantity of gas at a time, but for short periods of the day the volume jumped, as when the range was lit for preparation of a meal, or when range, water heater, and lights were all taking gas simultaneously. The meter had to meet the sudden peak. Problem: how to make a 5-light meter serve where otherwise a 30-light would be set.

In probably no other business was it so necessary for a manufacturer to be conservative. Accuracy and durability of product were the meter maker's prime concerns; ease and low cost of repair, the next requisite. The years had witnessed no radical departure from the design of the Glover type of consumer meter. Modifications in the nature of refinement and strengthening of construction, better materials for the parts, and highly developed skills had effected the improvements made up to 1900. A 5-light meter, for example, now had a working capacity of 114 cubic feet per hour with unchanged case size.

Gas engineers, demanding still greater efficient delivery, were somewhat critical of technological progress in meters in contrast with advances scored in other kinds of gas equipment. Association committees applied themselves to the task of remodeling construction features, either for increased capacity in continuous run or for increased reserve capacity only; but while the manufacturers stood ready to please all, the engineers were unable to reach harmony in their recommendations.

Since consideration must be given to wear on moving parts so as to preserve accurate registration and long life, the researches of American Meter followed a definite policy in this respect, arrived at in consultation with prominent engineers. This work started in 1903. A remodeled 5-light meter, commercially produced in 1906, incorporated larger diaphragms and heavier fittings, but retained the speed ratio of the old style although discharging 150 cubic feet per hour. It could take an overload of more than 50 per cent of rated capacity for reasonable periods. This was the origin of the so-called "B" meter.

The prefix B came about from the fact that American Meter, having completed its first million meters in 1899, designated its next serial numbers with the letter A. Several hundred thousand were already out under the new number series when the remodeled type was about to be produced, but the numerical order was not continued because of another circumstance. The Griffin company was then introducing its own enlarged meter bearing the letter A to indicate a special type. To avoid confusion, the parent company adopted the prefix B for its type.

The Griffin model worked at a higher speed and with larger valves and ports to gain the increased capacity. Sister companies contended over which was better, Griffin claiming 175-feet capacity. McDonald and Tufts made the B meter. So did Charles Dickey at Maryland, but he also put 10-light valves in a 5-light size, called this type "S" rather than "A," which would be copying Griffin's John Gribbel, and sold it for natural-gas use.

Frank Payne at Metric Metal looked askance. "There has been so much discussion during the past four years about 'Large Capacity' meters," said Metric's 1909 catalog in covering tincases, "that we have been making tests along these lines and have examined carefully a great many different makes of 'Large Capacity' meters, with the conclusion that, if long life and accuracy *are* any advantage, meters of Standard Capacity are the cheapest and best." Metric stood by standard capacity in standard sizes. Frankly, Payne was more interested in competing with his iron-case meters. Erie alone made them.

Later that year Metric Metal brought out a new series of iron-cases. Tobeys had been declining since 1904, their heyday: 60,000 produced, bringing the serial numbers to 230,559. The new iron-cases caught on slowly, but in a later B type, closely following the Glover design, they made substantial contributions to American's treasury.

B tincases were already selling in 30-, 60-, and 100-light sizes (the nomenclature still a misnomer, but state laws adhered to light ratings for meter proving). B's outsold A's. In time, Griffin made structural changes, enlarging the diaphragms and modifying gearing, so that capacity was no longer attained by high speed.

Coincidentally with the introduction of B tin meters, the Boston and Albany buildings were completed. Albany was equipped with tools to mass-produce many parts for the other factories to cut their costs. It so happened that metal prices were rising, affecting profit margin. A higher selling-price for meters was justifiable. The board of directors, however, viewed the situation

Structural drawing
of a two-diaphragm
slide-valve meter

Large meters (minus the fronts) of 6000-cu. ft. capacity at Maryland Meter

otherwise: "Our peculiar and intimate relations with our only customers, the gas companies, causes hesitation. We feel their interests, difficulties and prosperity are identical with our own, and as public opinion and in some cases the law prevent the gas companies from increasing their price, no matter what materials cost, we feel that we should be the last to raise them."

Gas sold at a dollar a thousand. Its cheapness was encouraging consumption.

Prepayment meters were now playing an important role in the more widespread use of gas, having opened hitherto unfriendly doors. They had also won over reluctant gas managers, who on reconsideration became eager to install a meter for the customer who used only a dollar's worth a month. They gained what they always sought—satisfied customers, no bills to quibble over, though not large customers, at least steady ones, paying cash in advance. Five-cent meters had been tried, after the English example of small coins, but nickels were not uniform in size. Besides, nobody expected much for a nickel apart from a trolley-car ride or a good cigar. As the grass-roots philosopher Mr. Dooley said, "Two drinks for a quarter is the standard of value." The quarter was the standard coin of the prepayment meter.

The superintendent of the Pawtucket (Rhode Island) Gas

Company told a meeting of the New England Gas Association that he had a thousand prepayment meters in use. "I would advocate by all means every gas man putting them in to accommodate a certain class of consumers." They were bringing an average monthly consumption close to that of regular meters supplying the same class.

In Eau Claire, Wisconsin, a town of sawmills and box factories, where wood for stoves was cheap and electricity gave competition, 95 per cent of new meters set were prepayments. They overcame the obstacle to gas stoves along with selling the latter on monthly installments. As against collection difficulties with other consumers, running sometimes to ninety days, the coin boxes were emptied about the twenty-third of the month, "which gives us a handsome bank balance with which to discount our bills."

Another function of prepayment meters, that of keeping dissatisfied consumers on the books, was related by the superintendent of the Consumers Gas Company in Woodbury, New Jersey. He bought his first two from a Tufts salesman for an experiment. One was set for the grumbling householder who was giving the most trouble; the other in the home of the company's secretary, as a check. "It was a success from the start," the superintendent reported. "It enables us to keep all the consumers. We have also

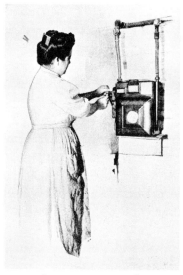

"Pay as you go on"

A Philadelphia gas fitter

added others with these meters. I am satisfied that they have increased our consumption of gas enough to more than offset the extra expense."

Being realistic, the superintendents mentioned unfavorable aspects as well. Pilfering from boxes was a pastime of sneak thieves. Or sometimes a consumer, being out of a quarter, dropped in a slug which might work; when the collector asked for a make-good, the consumer insisted it did not work and demanded it back. Sometimes a collector cut in on another man's route and helped himself. Others lost money or forgot to turn it in. "Ten collectors could gather ten thousand quarters and retain from three to five hundred coins without the company being able to trace the shortage. Changing routes, employing new help, in the long run doesn't change the situation."

It happened in Baltimore: A clever man in the ice business thought of freezing ice in the size and shape of a quarter. He tried it out and being of a neighborly sort extended the courtesy to his friends. When the meter man came around to collect, there was no quarter, just water.

The consensus of the gas companies was that the prepayment meter had done more than any other agency to increase consumption since the beginning of the industry. It opened up business they could not get without it. It appealed to a side of human nature that willingly bought in large quantity if small expenditures could be made at a time instead of a lump sum. Once-barren territories were now among the best revenue-producing. In the years before World War I, the tide of popularity was such that one-third of the meters being set were of the prepay type.

Griffin found a market for more than 1,500,000 three-light prepays and more than 1,500,000 five-light prepays before the close of 1910. Helme & McIlhenny sold its version in hundreds of thousands. McDonald supplemented its No. 1 Glover cartwheel mechanism with a No. 2 Glover version in response to a demand for a reliable outside attachment which a manufacturer or gas company could fit to old or new meters in the repair shop—and remove it without disturbance after it had served its purpose. McDonald also equipped meters with Griffin's S&P mechanism for those who preferred it. Maryland finally decided that the movement constructed under the S&P patents was the nearest approach to perfection. Griffin prepared for a continuing need for prepayment meters by reducing the attachment to a compact mechanism built inside the structure of 5-150-B and 5-175-A meters.

Some years elapsed before Metric Metal offered prepay assemblies on its new ironcases. Erie got ready meanwhile with another factory building—bolstering its claim to having the largest gas meter factory in the world—for an upsurge in natural gas.

Pennsylvania, long the leader in natural-gas production among seventeen states, was outdistanced in 1909 by West Virginia. A network of systems for gathering, transporting, and distributing served domestic and industrial users in northern West Virginia, western Pennsylvania, and virtually all of Ohio. Indiana's supply, once enormous but shamefully wasted through lack of metering, was nearly exhausted; Indiana had to revert to manufactured gas. West Virginia's gas was rich in heat units and was piped as far as Cincinnati and Pittsburgh.

More than two thousand natural-gas companies were now operating in the country as a whole. Heralding the development of the midcontinent area, producers in eastern Kansas formed the Kansas Natural Gas Company and piped into Kansas City and down to Joplin, Missouri. A wildcatter's discovery of the prolific Glenn Pool field in Oklahoma foretokened the spread of the area. The Gulf Coast region loomed as another source of natural gas with the Spindletop oil strike on a salt dome near Beaumont, Texas, the Caddo Field in Louisiana, and the Petrolia field in Texas. The Lone Star Gas Company carried gas 135 miles from Petrolia to Fort Worth and Dallas. Only the high expense of delivery limited the distance of transmission.

Mutual interests prompted the formation of a new association. In 1905, appliance manufacturers and local gas companies had organized the National Commercial Gas Association to foster a program of better merchandising methods for increasing the sales volume of stoves, water heaters, space heaters, laundry dryers, irons, and other appliances. The American Gas Light Association narrowed its scope to technical phases of the industry and merged the next year with the Western Gas Association and the Ohio Gas Light Association to form the American Gas Institute. This division of cooperative efforts occurred despite champions of the concept of consolidating all gas associations in a single strong body to represent the whole industry. The Natural Gas Associa-

Meter crew of Oklahoma Natural Gas Company, 1906

tion of America came into being, also in 1906, at a meeting in Kansas City.

Among the first members of that pioneer band in Kansas was a young man named Henry P. Westcott, whose wanderlust led him to Chanute from a village in western New York. His father had been a noted geologist, employed by Calvin Payne, and owner of a company that supplied the village with natural gas.

Westcott worked in Kansas fields as an independent meter tester. He took his brother-in-law, Henry N. Greis, a former bank teller back home, into partnership in 1907 and as Westcott & Greis they tested and repaired from West Virginia to Oklahoma. Their services were in lively demand, for gas no longer sold at the well at an annual flat rate. It issued in large volumes and at high pressures, but the quantity varied widely. Measurement was done by a proportional meter, which took a definite percentage off the line and passed it through a positive wet meter as a tally; by means of gearing, the index supposedly showed the total quantity.

Dirt usually interfered with the accuracy of the proportional meters then in use, and being complicated they made cleaning, repairing, and adjusting a problem. Westcott conceived an improvement on the valve plate that carried the interior parts. He fashioned a crude tin plate to his fancy and called on a meter maker in Pittsburgh with a view to getting it manufactured and sold in connection with a dry tally. Not satisfied that this firm could do the job properly, he thought of Metric Metal Works next because of its Tobey meter and close affiliation with the natural-gas business.

Rather than going directly to Frank Payne with his proposition, Westcott obtained employment at Metric as a factory hand, the better to size up Erie's capability. He was there only a short time before Payne noticed his name on the payroll and recognized the son of his father's late geologist. Westcott was summoned to the office.

The way Payne described the encounter to his family that evening, a fellow looking like a Western cowboy came in. "He brought an outlandish thing with him, but we're going to take it on and him with it."

The decision flew in the face of expert opinion. Donald McDonald, a son of William McDonald and an assistant general superintendent of American Meter, had used the expression "so-called proportional meter," in a public speech, saying, "To the meter maker educated to believe in the correct measurement of gas, there is no such thing." A recent McDonald catalog had not minced words either:

> Experience has demonstrated beyond question that gas in large quantities can be measured accurately and continuously only by a wet meter in which the measurement is accomplished by displacement. Devices claiming to measure by inference, by proportion, by the speed, pressure, or temperature of the passing gas are inaccurate, unreliable, and fallacious.

So said the station meter specialists. But Metric Metal's 1909 catalog gave the news:

> In placing the Westcott Proportional Meter on the market we have spared no expense to build an accurate meter of simplified construction. We have established a department in our factory devoted entirely to the manufacture of Propor-

tional Meters, where we are paying more special attention to testing than has ever before been given to Proportional Meter work. In addition to Flow-meters and large-capacity provers, we have installed an Oliphant Pilot Tube Measuring Apparatus.

Metric Metal announced its determination to "follow the subject of large volume measurement" as closely as it had done with domestic meters. The catalog, really a handbook on natural-gas operations, bore witness to the aim of identifying Metric as the leading center of information and service for this burgeoning branch of the industry. A second product was already available, the Westcott Patent Recording Volume and Pressure Gauge. Henry Westcott was under a free-wheeling arrangement that released his mechanical ingenuity and promotional zeal and brought to laboratory stage a practical orifice meter.

Foreshadowing the heavy contributions Metric was to make to American Meter's treasury through the sale of ironcase displacement and orifice meters, Frank Payne was elected in 1909 to fill a vacancy on the board of directors. The board met in Erie for

John B. McNary in his Hamilton, Ontario, office

the first time in March 1910 and heard a committee report on a new corporate lease on life.

American Meter had been incorporated in 1863 for a term of fifty years. In anticipation of the charter's expiration, a company named *The* American Meter Company was formed under the laws of New York, its duration perpetual, to acquire the assets of the existing concern and manufacture "articles pertaining to gas and water works." With capital stock of $8,000,000, it proposed to make the purchase for $5,950,000 in stock, this sum representing the excess over liabilities.

Stockholders voted approval of the sale to the new company and dissolution of the old, which had paid an average dividend of 7 per cent in the past ten years. Of the 54,602 shares voted, John Gribbel's 12,545 were the largest individual block. The Helme, McIlhenny, McDonald, and Dickey holdings numbered in the 3000s. Calvin Payne voted 400 shares; his Standard Oil associates, William Rockefeller and Charles W. Harkness, a little over 1000 each.

Other important business transacted on the day of dissolution was the appointment by the board of The American Meter Company of a committee to buy an automobile truck for the New York factory.

John McIlhenny was elected to continue as president. In rendering his report for the last year of the old company, he was pleased to observe that sales had passed the $3,000,000 mark. He reviewed the pleasant prospects of the gas companies ("with a proportionate demand for meters") and echoed their admission that "their success has been due to the accuracy and lasting qualities of the gas meter." He added, "I take pleasure in saying . . . on this vital point of accuracy and enduring qualities that all our factories are vying with each other in producing the best meter, and I believe that none better are produced in the world."

A disquieting note sounded in his last sentence: "With grateful thanks to you all, as officers and stockholders, for your kindness to me for the last sixteen years, I subscribe myself, John McIlhenny, President." The farewell it implied was made explicit soon after in a letter of resignation:

I feel that advancing years and my long service in this position demand from me this course, and that the affairs of

the Company should be placed in younger hands, I sincerely
believe. I fervently hope that my successor may have as long,
prosperous and agreeable experience as mine has been, and
see no reason why the Company should not go on prospering
even more in the future than in the past.

I do not wish to conceal my emotions when I have to lay
down this honorable position for the reasons given in the
beginning of this letter. . . . It is to me a special source of
gratification and consolation that in all our various proceed-
ings there has never been an unfriendly dispute or disagree-
ment, and that all our relations have been exceedingly
pleasant to me.

The letter, received by the board in May 1911, was tabled and
not taken up until November. Then Charles H. Dickey and
William E. Helme moved the election of Vice President John
Gribbel as the successor. Gribbel declined. He had financial stakes
in diverse enterprises, notably Curtis Publishing Company, and
said it would be impossible for him to serve. He and William
McDonald moved that Dickey be elected. The Baltimorean became the new president.

—6—

The Years Under Dickey

THE BUSINESS CALIBER OF CHARLES H. DICKEY, AMPLY DEMON-
strated in his management of Maryland Meter, had a special quality. If a phrase could characterize this trait, he was "restless to
rectify." Associates recalled his proxy fight in the Consolidated Gas
Company of Baltimore City back in 1900, when he was dissatisfied with a slow pace of modernization and demanded vigorous
action to promote gas for cooking and heating. Although owning
but a single share of that company's stock, he came near winning
a seat on the board. There was so much force in his arguments,
and in himself, that the directors elected Dickey to a vacancy a
few months later and in quick succession made him a member
of the executive committee (chairman of the committee by February 1901) and created the position of second vice president for
him. In the whirlwind, several thousand consumers were added,
a sliding scale of rates was adopted, stove and heater sales
multiplied.

C.H. liked color as well as action. At his suburban place in
Guilford he had a tally-ho, manned by a driver and an equerry
in red coats. It was his practice mornings to pick up friends on
the way to the city and deposit them at the Maryland Club. The
sight of the four horses drawing the coach and the sound of the
equerry's horn as they turned a corner was one of Baltimore's
memorable street scenes. C.H. did things with dash. On visits to
Boston as a director and president of Nathaniel Tufts Meter
Company, he took along a Negro chef to serve his colleagues
chicken à la Maryland.

Dickey was a capable public speaker, like other American
Meter spokesmen, before and after dinner (William McDonald,
for instance, had been called the Chauncey Depew of the American Gas Light Association). Dickey's talk at the second annual

Charles H. Dickey   Henry P. Westcott   Donald McDonald II

meeting of the American Gas Institute on "Obligations Imposed by the Possession of a Franchise" expressed his sense of public responsibility. He made the point that the rights of franchise holders "do not come before the rights of the people," and that the employees of utility companies must always recognize this.

His popularity was evidenced at the Institute's 1911 meeting in St. Louis, where conventioners holding "psalm books" sang new verses to current tunes. Along with *Every Little Movement* (the meter's movement) and *I'm Afraid to Go Home in the Dark* (the electric light failed), they sang, "Has Anybody Here Seen Dickey?" Known from shore to shore, Dickey of Baltimore:

> *It always makes us glad and gay*
> *To hear what the Dickey-bird has to say.*

On becoming president of The American Meter, he had much to say in the company's councils. The board empowered him to act as general agent with absolute authority over all the factories, particularly as to prices and conditions of sale. This was in line with a decision that "more active management in the general affairs of the Company must be taken." A plan was set in motion to keep the factories busy profitably on their individual work and to lower production costs by standardizing the inside parts supplied for their meters by Erie. The Philadelphia Arch Street factory, deemed superfluous, was closed and the equipment moved into Helme & McIlhenny.

As "adjustment of existing conditions" was the keynote of the new administration, a plan-and-scope committee was appointed to pave the way to full knowledge of costs, output, and sales. It recommended extension of Erie's cost accounting system to the other factories and a basis for computing interfactory prices. The committee consisted of Frank Payne, John D. McIlhenny, Harry A. Norton, now president of Tufts; Edmund S. Dickey, who was in charge at Maryland Meter since his brother's elevation; and W. Griffin Gribbel, son of John Gribbel and assistant manager of the Griffin plant.

C. H. Dickey kept his headquarters in Baltimore and commuted to New York. An office apart from the New York factory was opened at 105 West 40th Street. C.H. was on the go. He traveled to California in 1913 to look into the proposal of a promoter, who was short of capital, for combining gas companies in Santa Barbara, Santa Ana, and other communities. C.H. sensed the growth potential of the West Coast and was stirred by the arrival of natural gas, which had just come to Los Angeles over the mountains from the Buena Vista Hills. He went on to Chicago to convince the Dawes banking interests, and a group was formed, he included, to finance the Southern Counties Gas Company of California. None too happy about meter sales representation on the Coast, Dickey harbored the idea of a factory there.

The American Meter had recently purchased several meter firms in the East and Middle West, and liquidated some; the others also were due to be discontinued. A large acquisition was the Standard Meter Company in Philadelphia at 17th and Clearfield Streets, and with an eye to expanding production in that city a plot was bought next to it. New York no longer held attraction as a factory location.

The question of disposition of factories was one that Dickey pondered, but the outbreak of war in Europe in August 1914 put planning to rout, except that the board decided to stop manufacturing in New York. Depression bogged the country down for a year, causing a large loss in meter sales.

In 1916 the New York charter was given up. A corporation formed under the laws of Delaware, with the same name but minus the prefix "The," took over in an exchange of $6,090,000 in stock and with an additional payment of $2,030,000 in 6 per cent debentures. Directors and officers were unchanged.

The same year witnessed the passing of two stalwarts of the old guard. John McIlhenny, whose business history began with Colton & Code in 1848, had been a director continuously from 1895 until his death. William N. Milsted had been an officer in various posts since 1876.

Sales recovered somewhat from the low level of the preceding year, but the entry of the United States into the war in the spring of 1917 spread new confusion and confronted the company with the paramount problem of obtaining supplies. Again sales dipped. Dickey took up residence in New York to be close to daily developments. The gas industry was hard-pressed. While wartime increases in urban populations made the demand for gas soar, rising costs of materials, shortages of coal and oil, and difficulty in financing maturing obligations beset them in the face of fixed statutory rates for their product. American Meter felt the repercussions severely.

The gas industry, nevertheless, gave a significant push to the war effort. The United States Government lacked toluol, needed in making amatol for high explosives. When this country declared war, the entire toluol output of by-product coke-oven plants was under contract to the Allies for TNT. It was necessary to turn to companies producing manufactured gas and to extract toluol and benzol, the chemicals largely responsible for the luminosity of open-flame gas burners. Gas utilities in many cities undertook the operation of such recovery plants for Army Ordnance. In these places as much as half the consumers of gas for lighting had still been using open-flame tips. Conversion to mantles saved the situation; it preserved light and conserved gas.

The gas companies employed their customary advertising media to cooperate with wartime drives, in particular a campaign for home canning and food conservation. Besides displaying patriotic posters in district offices and on billboards, they held lectures and demonstrations for housewives in company rooms. It was a time also for collecting peach stones and coconut shells to be carbonized for poison-gas masks. Consolidated Gas of New York utilized its stations to make the carbon and soda lime that provided the filtering elements in masks worn at the front by the American Expeditionary Force.

In some states, public service commissions relented and permitted advances in gas prices. Washington was prevailed upon to give utilities priority on coal. The urgent need for a united voice for the industry brought to a head a movement to merge the American Gas Institute and the National Commercial Gas Association, and this was accomplished at a rally in June 1918 at the Engineering Societies Building in New York. The upshot was the American Gas Association. George B. Cortelyou, head of Consolidated Gas of New York and a versatile Cabinet member under President Theodore Roosevelt (last as Secretary of the Treasury), was elected president of the A.G.A.

Onerous restrictions on the gas companies continued. They were prevented by wartime regulations from extending their service lines. In the limp state of their finances many not only curtailed meter orders but had to be carried on open account. American Meter found it necessary to borrow considerable amounts from banks because of contracts for stock. Work in American Meter's factories became so scarce in 1918 that an attempt was made to obtain defense business in the nature of stamping and forming parts. It was a tardy attempt. Only a few minor government contracts remained available.

Payne was authorized by the board to represent American Meter at the Navy Department with a bid on 10,000 depth charges. The award came through in July, and Metric Metal went to work on it with other incidental war orders. Deadlines for delivery were met, but whether any of Erie's depth bombs saw service in that last year of the war is uncertain. Payne, however, was positive that the profit margin on the contract was excessive. He asked the Navy, on authority from the board, to let him reduce the price. The Navy objected. Payne wrote to President Woodrow Wilson. Permission finally came, and Payne said, "It was the hardest thing I ever did in my life."

The sales decline in 1918 was 54.5 per cent. Had it not been for Erie's production of ironcase meters, the loss would have been greater, but thanks to natural-gas needs and to development work, ironcases accounted for more than 21 per cent of the meter volume.

Metric Metal had tried to gain supremacy for its specialty in two new ways before the war. One was to overcome objection to the Tobey construction for measuring manufactured gas—

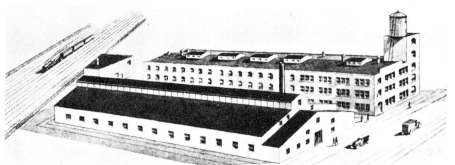

Helme & McIlhenny
on Clearfield St., Philadelphia

valve mechanism in the base, where condensation and dirt lodged
—by designing inverted Tobeys, making repairs easier. But this
did not stem the ebbing tide. The other effort was an A-type ironcase for large capacity. It was too big, too expensive to make, in
fact too good. It was supplanted in 1915 by a B ironcase for low-
and high-pressure service, the body cast in one piece, the mechanism closely adhering to Glover construction, first in 5-B and
10-B sizes, later in larger sizes. B-type high-pressure meters
(20-B) started in production in 1917 to meet a growing demand
as further discoveries of natural gas boosted this branch of the
business.

Frank Payne had foresight, and, through his father's influence,
a predisposition. His arrangement with Henry Westcott helped
him keep abreast of technical developments in the natural-gas
industry and put Metric Metal in the position of a vanguard, providing special products and publishing essential information.

The steps leading to the Westcott Orifice Meter were clear. To
measure very large volumes of natural gas at high pressure, a
method adapting the Pitot tube was introduced in 1910 by B. C.
Oliphant, then with the Iroquois Natural Gas Company in Buffalo. He calculated volume from the pressure of the flow and from
velocity. A less expensive layout and more versatile method was
sought by John G. Pew and H. C. Cooper of Peoples Natural Gas
Company, Pittsburgh. Their experiments in 1911 determined that
the theoretical formula evolved for pipeline flows by Thomas C.
Weymouth, of National Transit Company in Oil City, would
apply for an orifice meter—a plate put in the line, with readings
taken of the pressures on both sides and the differential converted

into cubic feet. Pew-Cooper differential connections were ready that summer to be tested for coefficients. Hired for the job was an engineer just graduated from Virginia Polytechnic Institute, James H. Satterwhite.

Satterwhite undoubtedly was the first man to install a recording orifice in the field. He ran tests on the main pipeline of Hope Natural Gas Company, of Sistersville, West Virginia, at the reducing station where the line entered Pittsburgh.

The scientific search went on. Metric Metal in 1912 set up a laboratory for large-volume, high-pressure measurement. A big frame building enclosed a 2200-cubic-foot holder, as a prover, and housed other equipment for determining the value of orifice coefficients and also for testing large-volume positive meters and proportional meters.

Westcott attended the Erie tests and had service tests run on his version of an orifice meter by Peoples of Pittsburgh. Weymouth at the same time was testing at Columbus, Ohio, for the right kind of pipe-tap connections. E. O. Hickstein was confirming data for the Wichita Pipe Line Company of Bartlesville, Oklahoma, out in Joplin.

The number of people engaged in natural gas had increased to such an extent that Payne felt justified in issuing a book on

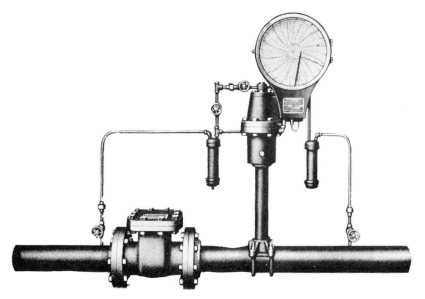

An orifice meter installation with a differential gauge

Holder and testing room, Metric Metal Works

the subject. Under the editorship of Westcott and the imprint of Metric Metal Works, the first edition of *Hand Book of Natural Gas* was published in 1913. It was a full-length book, 529 pages, covering production, transportation, and distribution, replete with tables and other data. The second edition (1915) was even longer, containing new and revised material.

Erie ran a series of calibrations on both large-capacity and smaller-capacity orifice meters. The Westcott Orifice Meter was put in service in 1915, with a Westcott Differential Gauge to record the drop in pressure from one side to the other. Up to this time few orifice meters were in use, mainly because the values of coefficients learned by operators were held confidential. Not until Hickstein presented his findings before the American Society of Mechanical Engineers in December of that year was the veil lifted.

Metric Metal decided that enough work in determining coefficients had been done and a suitable period of practical experience had elapsed to place them before gas companies generally. *Measurement of Gas by Orifice Meter*, authored by Westcott and published in 1918, presented complete data in book form for the first time. With the Wichita company's permission, it included

Hickstein's paper, "The Flow of Air Through Thin Plate Orifices," thus making the coefficients available as a matter of public record. Westcott transposed them from curves to tables so that non-engineers also could use them. Data was given on pipe-tap connections which Metric adopted after the Joplin tests. The book became the standard reference for midcontinent operators.

Westcott was intimately acquainted with the natural-gas leaders of the day. He helped them and was well-liked. In the large Erie laboratory, dubbed "the chapel," he trained young men in meter work who were gas company employees. In the literary output for his encouraging publisher were *Hand Book of Casinghead Gas*, brochures, and instruction circulars—a flow keeping up with the flow of gas.

The book on casinghead gas in 1916 reflected another facet of Westcott's ranging mind and promotional spirit. This gas, coming up through oil sand with oil, and formerly allowed to waste in the atmosphere or burned in flambeau torches, contained precious natural gasoline. The foolhardiness of sending the high-grade fuel up in smoke gave way to a rapidly growing extraction industry, as gasoline buggies came into vogue and blazed a trail to the automobile market. Westcott visited many gasoline plants; was permitted to see their reports and check for accuracy. His book was issued in a small first edition, anticipating swift changes while recognizing present needs. The third edition in 1922 was to make a jump from the 274 pages of the first to 672 pages.

Among the sequels to interest in casinghead gas was Westcott's formation of his own American Gasoline Company and hiring of an engineer named John C. Diehl to work for him in a garage across the street from the Metric factory. The Westcott Large Capacity and Casinghead Gas Meter followed. Of far-reaching significance, natural gasoline extraction methods led scientists to the separation of propane and butane and the compression of these hydrocarbons as bottled gas for distribution in areas beyond the reach of gas mains.

A selling agency in Tulsa for the midcontinent region was appointed by C. H. Dickey. Henry Greis had moved to that city, lured from Chanute by the center of Oklahoma oil operations and by oil itself, but continuing Westcott & Greis as a meter-testing firm. James Satterwhite had joined the trek of thousands of eastern oil and gas men to the fields of the Southwest, and managed

gas properties in Oklahoma towns. Satterwhite learned on a visit
to Tulsa in 1917 that Westcott & Greis was going to act as broker
for products applicable to the natural-gas industry, and after
fifteen minutes' talk with Greis he was hired as the salesman.
They handled Westcott proportional and orifice meters among
other items. The next year, Satterwhite went to St. Louis to meet
Dickey and acquired for his boss the exclusive territory agency
for American Meter products excluding positive meters.

The war over, Dickey had definite ideas on the future course
of American Meter. Surveying its inheritance of factories from
the consolidation of the 1890s, he held that the time had come for
concentration of facilities. Philadelphia should have only one
producing factory—close down Helme & McIlhenny at once,
Griffin as soon as possible, and retain and enlarge the plant on
Clearfield Street. Station meters should be made only in Philadelphia. Albany should not try to increase its business. No change
was needed in Boston; Tufts had been dissolved as a corporation
in 1917 and integrated as the Nathaniel Tufts Meter Works.
Experimental apparatus work should be moved from Philadelphia
to New York. Baltimore had a sufficient plant to produce all
B-type meters and should supply the Chicago district while Philadelphia took care of the eastern district. Dickey's comment on
Erie was that its cost of manufacture was too high.

Dickey placed his views before the board of directors a week
after the armistice. He said "a vast saving to the company and a
tremendous reduction in our overhead" would result. A committee headed by John Gribbel considered his recommendations and
approved most of them. But the plan did not proceed precisely
as contemplated. Helme & McIlhenny prepared to move out of
Cherry Street a year later, and as it turned out, the Race Street
factory occupied by Griffin survived Maryland Meter. At any rate,
concentration was considered a good thing.

Although sales rebounded in 1919 and broke the prewar record,
and climbed even faster in 1920, Dickey was far from satisfied.
His heart was in California. The performance of Pacific Meter
Company, American Meter's selling unit, sorely needed bolstering. Dickey pressed his fellow directors to provide a better working basis with Southern California gas companies by establishing
facilities in Los Angeles for proving, topping, and painting.
Actually, he wanted a full-fledged factory on the Coast.

Dickey moved to California in 1921. Pacific Meter was liquidated and Pacific Meter Works was established. Winning his point on a factory, he next had to steer a course between the hot rivalries existing between the northern and southern halves of the state for population and industrial growth. The Pacific Gas and Electric Company persuaded him to set up the factory in San Francisco, leaving him to exercise diplomacy in soothing the southern companies with an efficient Los Angeles service station. The new plant was opened in 1922, Dickey installed as manager. He was still president of American Meter, but the next two annual reports were signed by Gribbel, the vice president.

Chairman of the board from 1923 to 1927, Dickey spent his California golden years solidifying the position of Pacific Meter Works and participating in the activities of the Pacific Gas Association, of which he was president in 1928. After the Pacific Lighting Corporation bought the Southern Counties Gas Company he became a director and large stockholder of the parent company. He was a director also of Pacific Gas and Electric. When he retired from the meter business he said that the increasing pressure of American Meter duties would not permit him to enjoy leisure in California. The business had expanded to more than $10,000,000 in annual sales.

Promoting "new business" in Chicago:
a float in the Prosperity Day parade, 1911

Domestic Demonstration Department of Brooklyn Union Gas Company, 1911; *(below)* holding class in an outlying community, 1925

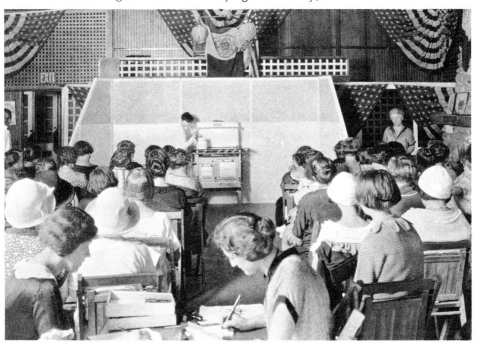

—7—

When Gribbel Was President

THE PROSPEROUS 1920S DID NOT COME OF A SUDDEN. POSTWAR inflated costs of materials and labor caught public service companies in a vise of old fixed rates, preventing them from earning a proper return on investment. Some resorted to receivership in self-protection. American Meter, dependent on gas companies for its business, made their battles its own and not only helped carry them—accounts receivable rose to $1,500,000—but contributed to the American Gas Association Emergency Fund in 1920 for a campaign for rate increases and other relief. Lack of home-building activity, in a general recession that hit the country, added to the woes in stifling normal growth of gas service connections.

A relief measure the A.G.A. agitated for was complete abolishment of candlepower requirements in state and municipal regulations governing gas companies. They were no longer realistic. They caused an unjust burden of expense.

The illuminating quality of gas originally was determined by a standard known as the English Parliamentary Sperm Candle, adopted throughout the United States. Photometers to measure for the standard were sold by Samuel Down and other early meter makers and their successors. The science of photometry advanced with the design of the Ten Candle Power Pentane Lamp, which the Metropolitan Gas Referee of London adopted as official in 1898 and which leading American companies employed in their testing. Pentane lamps were made and advertised by American Meter, and their use spread. Meanwhile, the Welsbach mantle, utilizing the Bunsen burner for incandescence, had given importance to the thermal or heat-producing quality of gas. Candlepower began losing significance.

American Meter became the sole U.S. manufacturer of the Junkers Calorimeter for the measurement of calories or British

John Gribbel   F. H. Payne and John C. Diehl

thermal units. This company modified the construction for easier
yet accurate operation to the satisfaction of the old American
Gas Institute and public authorities. Although cooking and water
heating with gas assumed the greater part of consumption as
electric lighting gained favor, official recognition of heating value
as the standard of gas quality came slowly. Wisconsin was first
in 1908. Here and there other public service commissions conceded that the requirement of twenty candles per cubic foot was
obsolete and specified BTUs instead. But in many states the
anachronism lingered. The A.G.A. aimed to put it in limbo, for in
order to attain the legal level of candlepower it was necessary to
enrich gas with expensive oil.

The campaign succeeded. One by one the remaining commissions changed to thermal units; New York City was the last in
1922. Public opinion also supported the justice of the drive for
revised rates. As the financial condition of the utilities improved,
a further boost was given by nationwide resumption of housing
construction that took up the wartime slack and increased the
number of metered homes.

"One Thousand Uses for Gas." "You Can Do It Better With
Gas." Slogans adopted by the industry and individual utilities
spearheaded drives in thousands of communities. Local companies instituted regular weekly cooking demonstrations and

offered door prizes of the cooked food. They set up home service departments, accenting the planning of meals for families, as did women's magazines, but did not overlook putting across the commercial message with showrooms for appliances.

The companies went beyond the home, into hotels and restaurants. Also, backed by a defense-production record of forging, heat-treating, and annealing by gas, they promoted industrial fuel. (During the recession the increased use of gas in industrial operations offset American Meter's decline in sales of domestic-size meters.) Sliding scales for larger users were the non-secret weapon in these successful campaigns for volume consumption. The lighting load was down to 21 per cent in 1920, to 15 per cent in 1925, while the industrial fuel load rose in those years from 25 per cent of the total to 29 per cent of a much higher over-all total.

The home, however, stayed always in mind. A fascinating thought was the possibility of central house heating by manufactured gas. Baltimore Consolidated had acted on it before the war by experimenting with what was available—gas-fired boilers designed for natural gas—and installed an altered version in hundreds of homes on a low secondary rate. The experience pointed up the need for more intensive study of heating methods and equipment.

An A.G.A. survey in 1921 showed seven million gas cooking appliances in homes, about one and a half million gas water-heaters, close to a million gas space-heaters. Progress certainly had been made in design, insulation, heat controls and clock controls for ovens, burner arrangements, pilots, and good looks— white enamel ranges, even tints. New appliances were streaming into the market in such profusion that the A.G.A. formed a committee on standardization of appliance specifications. In 1923 its executive board approved a new plan to insure safe and satisfactory gas service to consumers through research, formulation of standards, and testing of products.

Cleveland was selected as the location for an appliance testing laboratory because both manufactured and natural gas were used there. The East Ohio Gas Company offered one of its buildings for temporary quarters. The manufacturers' section of the A.G.A. promised to furnish equipment, American Meter pledging apparatus, meters, and other articles of its manufacture.

The A.G.A. Central Testing Laboratory started functioning in

Demonstration truck of The Peoples Gas Light and Coke Company, Chicago, 1923; *(below)* heating and refrigeration promotion, 1928

1925. Raymond Conner, of the Portland (Oregon) Gas and Coke Company, chairman of the Pacific Gas Association's appliance testing code committee, was the director. In little more than a year 14 types of flexible tubing, 44 space heater models, and 1715 ranges were approved. The requirements they met were those prepared by A.G.A. committees and endorsed by the American Society of Mechanical Engineers and the American Engineering Standards Committee. The A.G.A. committees consisted of manufacturers and gas company engineers, representatives of the U.S. Bureau of Standards and Bureau of Mines, the Public Health Service, and the Masters Plumbers Association of America, and other qualified persons.

Within the same period tentative requirements had also been worked out for water heaters and house heating equipment. Standards for the latter were prepared by a group headed by Eugene D. Milener, who had done the research on this subject for Baltimore Consolidated and developed the Degree-Day method of calculating heating load.

The public's confidence in gas appliances strengthened because, in looking for the seal of approval, people bought wisely. Calls for product testing taxed the facilities of the laboratory and staff. A permanent building was erected in Cleveland in 1928 and subsequently a sister laboratory in Los Angeles. Research was being pursued along many lines, including gas as fuel for a system to produce cold air for air conditioning. "One Thousand Uses for Gas."

As the industry grew, so grew American Meter. Mutual prosperity was the essence of the company's existence. But holding leadership in its branch of the industry was not a matter of sharing in the fruits through size; rather, the rewards stemmed from esteem earned by a policy of durable dependability. Company philosophy was epitomized in the credo John Gribbel wrote in a Griffin catalog:

> An order placed with us is more than a business transaction for the purpose of making money. It is a trust reposed in our integrity and skill. We expect satisfied customers, but we ourselves are not satisfied until the last jot and tittle of obligation and responsibility on our part is discharged.

Gribbel was elected president of American Meter in 1923, when Dickey resigned to focus his talents on developing the Pacific Meter Works as a strong producing unit, with zealous faith in the future of the West Coast. Like Dickey, Gribbel had a substantial direct financial interest in the gas business, being virtual owner of the Tampa (Florida) Gas Company, and his large fortune encompassed other industrial holdings. Gribbel was a conservative man with forceful opinions. He spoke of "the conservatism which has marked our company's operations. We have not departed from the ancient landmarks."

Unwilling to have a private office and detachment from the workaday world of the Griffin plant, Gribbel occupied a corner of a large room in which ten other persons worked. Here on Race Street he performed his duties as head of the company while keeping up competition with Helme & McIlhenny over on Clearfield Street, the D. McDonald & Co. Works, and Maryland Meter Works. Gribbel persisted in the conviction that independent units gave American Meter strength.

Each of the six factories made a uniform tincase meter—Metric Metal more concerned with ironcases—and kept its own books, sending monthly reports and money to the treasurer's office. All except Tufts were conducted almost as though they were continuing individual family businesses. Gribbel's son, W. Griffin Gribbel, was his plant manager. Helme had John D. McIlhenny, Jr., as manager. Dickey's brother Edmund was running the Baltimore factory, two sons of William McDonald held the fort in Albany, and Frank Payne ruled the roost in Erie.

By the same token the officers of the company were as widespread, with C. H. Dickey, who had been appointed chairman of the board, extending the slate to California. Harry Norton became vice president on Gribbel's elevation; he remained at Tufts in Boston, ably assisted since 1898 by his brother Arthur. The oversight of Payne was quickly remedied by amending the bylaws for an additional vice president. The assistant treasurer since 1903, Francis W. Benson, a brother-in-law of Treasurer Helme, was of course in Philadelphia.

William McDonald died in 1922 at the age of seventy-nine. One of the original movers and founders of the 1895 consolidation, he had served as secretary for the past ten years. His son Donald, who had already succeeded him as general superintendent of the company, became secretary as well.

Each factory had punched out its own tincases and manufactured meters completely before World War I, but production economies were instituted in the 1920s. Maryland Meter, which put up a new building to replace a structure no longer strong enough, acquired a toggle joint stamping press of great size that did a number of operations simultaneously and in two or three weeks' time could take care of an entire year's requirements of all the plants. Besides this, Maryland made large-meter parts for them. Metric Metal took over the manufacture of indexes for all.

After meter production in New York had ended, apparatus was still made there. Now it was transferred to Albany, all such work brought under Donald McDonald. Albany made meter provers, calorimeters, hydrometers, wet test meters, gauges, and other articles for customers of the several factories. With the transfer went an expert toolmaker, Ernest Kerstein, who had contributed meter refinements while in New York and merited a machine shop to himself. He developed a new flag carriage with a bridgeplate, Bakelite insert valve guide, also cast-in valve seats and crank step (instead of soldering), an idea that was to lead to the important innovation of die-casting valve tables complete and to afford fixed points.

Albany set the pace in sewing diaphragm skins. An age-old practice of meter makers, after the skins were tanned and cemented, was to have neighborhood women come in and take them home for blindstitching and hand crimping. Albany devised a blindstitch sewing machine for this purpose and supplied Boston with finished diaphragms, tied onto rings and affixed with discs.

It was at the McDonald factory that Griffin Gribbel had entered the meter business in 1904, as a draftsman. Next he became a salesman for the Griffin factory and then assistant manager. After the war he helped the gas associations of Pennsylvania and New Jersey survive the critical years by initiating the Eastern States Gas Conference as a geographic division of the A.G.A. He became manager of the Griffin factory in 1924. A fervent association man, he headed the manufacturers' section of the A.G.A. one year and filled a place on the organization's executive board and executive council.

Newly assigned to Albany as assistant manager was Norton McKean, a nephew of Harry Norton. He had joined Tufts in

Arthur E. Norton   Harry A. Norton   Norton McKean

1913 and risen to superintendent. Three years after being in the
new post he was appointed Albany manager.

Among recruits in the ranks were a pair of former naval avia-
tion pilots, who began their meter careers in Baltimore. Edmund
Dickey hired Alexander McW. Wolfe in 1919 and also his friend,
C. Benson Dushane, Jr., in 1920. Wolfe shortly became an assistant to Edmund, and then engineer and assistant manager.
Dushane's first assignment was to make the drawings for a C
meter, designed to double the capacity of a 3200-foot B by putting
in double-expansion diaphragms and lengthening the valves (it
cut the customer's cost). After a brief period as Maryland's
superintendent, he was named traveling representative of the
Chicago agency. Wolfe gained selling experience too. On a visit
to New Orleans he encountered three other American Meter
salesmen in the gas company's outer office—and won the order.

The salesmen met again in Erie, with other factory and agency
representatives, this time for the first annual sales conference in
1925, held at clubs in town and in Payne's "chapel." Gribbel presided at the opening session.

On this occasion Harry Norton expounded a four-point system
of meter maintenance for gas companies, which he had derived
from analyses of records made on thousands of meters sent to
Tufts for repair. The utilities' practices regarding meters on their
lines were varied and usually random. He concluded that there

should be a periodical testing date for all consumer meters—it was not good to keep a meter in service until it broke down—and also a rule for condemning those that had outlived their usefulness.

Norton recommended, and urged the salesmen to do likewise, a seven-year test period. He said idle meters should not be removed within that time because of the expense. He favored a fourteen-year periodical repair date; no diaphragm should be left in longer. Small-capacity and old, wornout meters brought in should be condemned forthwith. These were Norton's "Four Cardinal Points," which he espoused in lectures and pamphlets. The average consumer's home with its various appliances had a peak-demand load far exceeding the capacity of old three-light and five-light meters, whose continued use caused a strain on the working parts, lost motion, and loss of registration. To attempt to replace worn parts in old meters and fit them with new diaphragms that would outlast them would cost virtually as much as a new meter of greatly increased capacity and strength.

Convinced of the Four Cardinal Points, utilities adopted procedures for keeping meter test records, analyzing performance, and reducing maintenance costs. They went on condemnation programs, for it was far more economical to throw out meters that needed much repair and anyway would soon become inadequate. The companies had justification in ordering replacements. As a consequence, the sales of American Meter factories stepped up considerably.

The high spots in sales and net profit were hit in 1926. A sizable portion of the income was provided by Canadian Meter Company. Pacific Meter Works, which moved out of a rented factory and erected a new one in San Francisco, and built and enlarged a service station in Los Angeles, flourished with the progress of the West Coast. Metric Metal Works had introduced curb meters, a variation on the ironcase, set in concrete boxes below the ground between curb and sidewalk for accessibility without entry into premises; they were popular in Florida, Oklahoma, and California. And natural-gas production and transmission, taking giant strides, called for large numbers of orifice meters.

One gloomy note was the decline in station meters. Daily output in manufactured-gas cities had grown to vast proportions,

Meeting of American Meter Company in Erie, June 20, 1929

Front row, left to right: Francis I. Thompson, John C. Diehl, Carl Asendorf, Harry Cartwright, Guy Ballentine, Edwin Bates, F. H. Wells, Donald McDonald, John Gribbel, Francis H. Payne, William D. Dickey, Spencer Hamme, Eugene Metz, A. M. Doty, Albert Barrett, Arno Huettig, John B. McNary, Calvin N. Payne II, W. V. Stockton, Jr.

Back row, left to right: Frank Hart, Kenneth C. Tomlinson, Charles Bollinger, F. H. Oliphant, James H. Satterwhite, Mett Bailey, Julius Bruder, Jack Montgomery, Norton McKean, John D. McIlhenny, Jr., Alexander McW. Wolfe, C. Benson Dushane, Jr., R. Wallace McClenahan, R. E. Fetzer, Charles T. Rodgers, Arthur E. Norton, John Van Norden, William H. Kaiser, Charles Prior, Garrett B. Linderman, Jr.

necessitating expensive foundations and structures to house multiple units of these meters. It was perhaps inevitable that another
device would come along and put the station meter into discard.
Competitors with a blower type that occupied one-tenth of the
space of a wet meter found favor in the early 1920s. American
Meter was negligent in reading the sign of the times. In hopes
of recapturing station business the company sponsored research
by Garrett B. Linderman, Jr., on his conception of a variable
orifice meter.

Henry Westcott had re-entered the Westcott & Greis partnership in Tulsa with Henry Greis and James Satterwhite. His
scientific aide, John Diehl, began dividing time between him and
Metric Metal in 1921. Diehl redesigned the Westcott Orifice
Meter, which cost too much to make and had to be individually
calibrated. The Erie factory decided to manufacture Diehl's
improved model, and the Tulsa agency's monthly sales began
to oustrip its former annual figure. For better coverage of the
midcontinent market, a warehouse was set up in Dallas with
Harold W. Wahl in charge.

Diehl helped Westcott prepare the third edition of *Hand Book
of Casinghead Gas* and shared the title page of the second edition
of *Measurement of Gas and Liquids by Orifice Meter*, both published in 1922. Not altogether a bookman and laboratory recluse,
Diehl made many trips out in the field. At Port Arthur, Texas,
he was apparently the only man without firearms; people carried
guns, and oil refineries had to be guarded by Texas Rangers to
keep the unruly from interfering. In Arizona he met Oklahoma
oilmen drilling and wondered why they were there. They told him
Oklahoma was "all played out."

The truth was that the world's largest dry-gas field, Hugoton
in southwestern Kansas, stretching across Oklahoma into Texas,
had recently been discovered. Texas was in a fair way of taking
the lead from Oklahoma as the largest natural-gas producer. This
became a certainty after the tremendous Amarillo field in the
Panhandle was opened, although a fairly comparable reserve at
Monroe in northern Louisiana came in at the same time. That
year, 1925, technology synchronized with nature to give long-
distance natural-gas transmission its real start: seamless, electrically welded pipe reducing friction and permitting increased
diameter became available. The natural-gas industry had already

Under a blazing Texas sun with sections of pipeline en route to central Indiana, 1930

passed one trillion cubic feet in annual consumption versus 339 billion in 1906 and 753 billion in 1916. Its future loomed as big as the reserves.

The Natural Gas Association of America began a study of measurement by orifice meters in 1924 with the cooperation of the American Society of Mechanical Engineers and the U.S. Bureau of Standards. The American Gas Association also entered on a series of tests to determine the correct method of installing these meters and the factors and operative requirements for their use. Henry Westcott died that year, and Frank Payne was authorized by his board of directors to employ Diehl full-time as an engineer. The demand for *Hand Book of Natural Gas* had just about exhausted the third edition. Payne's brother, Christy Payne, in charge of natural gas for Standard Oil, urged Frank to bring the book up to date and have Diehl write it. Diehl undertook a complete revision of the data previously published on the subject —Christy read it in manuscript—and the new book, issued in 1927 as *Natural Gas Handbook* became the authoritative text. Industry contracts were tied to its tables.

One hundred and seventy miles from the Monroe field, gas was piped to Baton Rouge; 250 miles, from the Panhandle to Wichita. The Monroe line was extended to New Orleans. Transmission lines were being connected: Amarillo through to Denver, 454 miles of twenty-inch and twenty-four-inch pipe. The El Paso Natural Gas Company was formed to pipe and distribute from

Welding pipe on the 1929 line from Jal, New Mexico, to El Paso

gas wells in southeastern New Mexico to its home city, and thrust its system into southern California. Also in California, huge gas wells near Elk Hills and Kettleman Hills were linked to serve the San Francisco Bay area. Natural gas packed about twice as many heat units. The Pacific Gas and Electric Company, like utilities in other regions converting from manufactured gas, had the task of adjusting the appliances of the consumers on its lines.

As changeovers proceeded in cities penetrated by pipelines, accelerated renewal of meter diaphragms took place. The diaphragms, having absorbed condensates of manufactured gas, were at the mercy of the dryness of natural gas, which sucked out the chemicals and lessened flexibility. American Meter improved the dressing, also experimented with rubberized fabric to replace leather. Testing was prolonged. The company did not propose its substitute at once because of a policy—the conservatism that Gribbel epitomized—of building up years of experience before pushing a new product.

Recognition of the overlapping if not identical interests of the

Building the pipeline from the Kettleman Hills to San Francisco, 1929

two national gas associations induced the leaders to form a more perfect union. The groups were amalgamated in 1927, retaining the name of American Gas Association.

Natural-gas consumption advanced at so rapid a clip that it totaled 1.9 trillion cubic feet by 1930, much being used in industrial functions. The business was touched with magnitude. Almost every news report concerning it was astonishing. The Lone Star Gas gathering and distributing system (originated by Calvin Payne in 1909 as a single line from Petrolia to Fort Worth and Dallas) spread over hundreds of communities in Texas and Oklahoma. From the Texas Panhandle a twenty-four-inch pipeline carried gas in 1931 to meet mounting consumer demands a thousand miles away in Chicago. Another Texas line shot out to Rockville, Indiana, and connected there to cities in the East.

Even as a new day dawned for the gas industry, a foreshadow of the great economic depression of the 1930s crept up. Meter sales as a whole began slipping prior to the symptomatic crash of the stock market. They plummeted in 1931 and 1932. American

One of the first long-distance, 24-inch pipelines: from the Texas Panhandle to Chicago, crossing Iowa in 1930

Meter entered a period of change.

Two stalwarts of the old guard were gone. William E. Helme, treasurer since 1895, died in 1929. Harry A. Norton, the company's key figure in New England since 1896, had died two years before. Both men had been torchbearers of the American Meter tradition.

Exigencies of the times brought to a head the centralization of Philadelphia production envisioned long ago by C. H. Dickey, and prompted factory realignment beyond his plan. In 1932 Helme & McIlhenny and John J. Griffin & Company ceased as entities. They were consolidated at Race Street. Tufts' stamping plant was dismantled, its requirements taken over by Albany, which also got jurisdiction of New York business. The moves were made with a view to building up Philadelphia and Albany as production centers. Baltimore was doomed.

The Dickey influence had vanished, C.H. having sold his stock. His son William resigned as manager of Pacific Meter

Works. The status of his brother Edmund became uncertain after
the board of directors appointed a special committee in 1934 to
advise on the closing of Maryland Meter. The committee, con-
sisting of McDonald, McKean, and Diehl (named to the new
post of company chief engineer in 1929), recommended speedy
dismantling of the Baltimore factory and transfer of its tools to
Albany and Erie. Alexander Wolfe was sent to Boston as assistant
manager under Arthur Norton. Edmund Dickey was proposed as
general salesmanager, a position not yet existing, but received the
title of executive representative.

Maryland Meter shut down in the fall of 1934 after a long life
of supplying a substantial portion of American Meter's products.
The special committee said that to compensate for the loss of its
production, the Philadelphia factory also should have adequate
facilities, but that Philadelphia was not well organized to cope
with additional business efficiently. The records showed that its
operating profit was lower than Baltimore's though its volume
was larger. Philadelphia needed to be reorganized, and, to avoid
embarrassment, President Gribbel should be relieved of factory
details, the committee said. "We venture the suggestion that he
be made comfortable in the Treasurer's office." (Gribbel was
additionally treasurer, after Benson, who was in that post two
years, died by drowning.) "The Committee appreciates that this is
asking a great deal, but the spirit in which the suggestion is made
is sincere and, if agreeable to the President, will in a large way
provide a freedom of action which the Committee feels is quite
necessary."

Gribbel was seventy-six years old. He stepped aside with grace
and let the special committee work out the problems in Race
Street—changes in production methods, closer interfactory cooperation with regard to surplus output and disposal, and a
program to enable Erie to supply parts requirements anticipated
by Philadelphia, Albany, Boston, and San Francisco. The segments of American Meter were on the long road to coordination.

—8—

Progress in a Depression

THE CHANGING NATURE OF THE GAS INDUSTRY, WITH ITS PROBLEMS of pressure regulation, determination of the flow of gas wells, transmission under high pressure, measurement in enormous volumes, and flow control, presented American Meter with new fields for research and usefulness. At the same time came developments in the refining of crude petroleum, extraction of gasoline and liquefied petroleum gases, also calling for research, engineering, and special instruments. Here were opportunities for the company to widen its activities and become less sensitive to the fluctuating demand for positive displacement meters. Thus, while taking steps to streamline the factory setup for tincase production, American Meter diversified.

The company entered a new field of manufacture—pressure regulators—toward the end of 1931 by forming a subsidiary, Reliance Regulator Corporation.

California was the backdrop for the story. Thaddeus Lowe, inventor of the water-gas process, who had moved to Pasadena early in the century, might well be considered the instigator. The gas company organized by him there and managed by his son instructed a local foundry and machine shop to make the parts for what became the first Reliance regulators. A schoolboy, Walter Thrall, was employed by Lowe after hours to assemble and test them. In those days of low-pressure manufactured gas, the spread of population to outlying districts often required gas plants to raise the distribution pressure, yet hold it down for areas nearby. The Edison Company in Santa Barbara, requiring conversion to semi-high pressure, ordered regulators from the Pasadena shop, and young Thrall got a hand in manufacturing. Before long he was in charge, designing and producing various types of regulators for specific needs. Right after World War I,

Thrall was called back from other employment; the new owner, Walter M. Thompson, formerly an iron manufacturer, depended on him to help get orders from California companies wanting to step up the pressure in their old gas mains.

This business was operated as Reliance Regulator Company, with Reliance Iron Works as its foundry. For sales representation in the Southwest, an agency agreement was made with James Satterwhite of Westcott & Greis, who thereupon in the 1920s influenced utilities in his region to adopt intermediate pressure regulation in smaller pipes.

Another concurrent development was a propane-butane mixture called "Rockgas," introduced by Andy Kerr, who needed regulators for it. Reliance converted its high-pressure natural-gas regulator for his use, and became involved in the liquefied petroleum gas business. With bottled gas, the trade practice arose of selling cylinders to the consumer in pairs, one cylinder connected to the stove by a valve, its mate held in reserve; when the stove went out, the user opened the valve of the second cylinder. Wanted: an automatic device and indicating gauge for change-over from empty to full for continuous service, the indicator signaling that a fresh bottle should be ordered. Reliance was first to develop an LP automatic throwover regulator.

By 1927 Reliance had outgrown its manufacturing facilities. A new plant was built in Alhambra, California. In answer to gas companies' needs for versatility to permit conversions for a variety of services, Reliance developed the combination-balanced-valve regulator with a valve body on which they could assemble many combinations with parts which it supplied. Thrall was still responsible for most of the designs.

Reliance's leadership in the regulator field and its creativeness drew Frank Payne to Alhambra in 1930. Negotiations for acquisition followed, culminating the next year. Into the corporation that was organized to take over, American Meter put $500,000, Thompson $150,000. He continued as president, Thrall as chief engineer. American had made its first move to diversify. Not much later it was producing Reliance regulators in Erie for customers in the East.

On the heels of the acquisition, American Meter bought from Henry Greis in 1932 all the outstanding stock of Westcott & Greis. The manager of the Tulsa office and warehouse was Cade

Measuring station at Joliet, Ill., 1931 with installation of Westcott Orifice Meters

C. Clover, while Harold Wahl now handled the southern division from Houston. They had a trained corps of engineers covering the gas and oil fields, with assists from John Diehl. Tests were run at Port Arthur for the Gulf Oil Company to get the proper factors for measuring various types of crude, in one instance underwater oil pumped to off-shore boats. The question was whether this kind of measurement could be done, as data on viscosity were lacking. Diehl heard that the data could be obtained in Los Angeles. He hied there, didn't find the information satisfactory, so returned to Port Arthur for further tests. He compiled oil coefficients. And Gulf bought meters.

Diehl's philosophy was, "Help the other fellow and you'll get the business."

On another occasion he was asked to solve the problem of measuring flow in the odd-size sections of a telescopic pipeline delivering natural gas to a refinery in Beaumont, Texas. He sat up all night to figure it out and came up with a method permitting direct reading from a chart.

Besides contributing the Square Root Chart, which reduced the possibility of reading errors, and the Square Root Integrator, Diehl was responsible for devices that proved large-capacity positive displacement meters under actual working pressure conditions. One was the Low Pressure Flow Prover, using an orifice meter method; it led to an increase in the rate of flow at which tests could be made. Another was the Critical Flow Orifice Prover, applied for higher pressures.

There was more to come from this fertile, practical mind. Encouraged by the company to communicate knowledge, Diehl edited *Handbook on Measuring Gas by Positive Displacement* (1930) and its successor, the first edition of *Handbook E-4* (1936). In the interim he designed a mechanical integrator, the Double Integrating Orifice Meter, which gave a totalized indication for all rates of flow or variations in pressure, particularly desirable where gas was sold to industrial plants and the quantity passed needed to be determined daily or hourly. The principle was next applied for devices attached to displacement meters: a Base Pressure Index, correcting the measured volume to standard cubic feet at the base pressure, and a Base Volume Index, including a correction for temperature. Automatic multiplication of the factors did the trick.

Preceding these innovations, Garrett Linderman, in Metric Metal's Erie laboratory, where orifice meter research was concentrated, worked on his patented integrator for measuring large volumes of manufactured gas as a substitute for station meters. A thirty-inch model, placed experimentally in the Astoria station of Consolidated Gas of New York, was accepted by that company. American Meter had made its last station meter installation. The Linderman meter was an engineering feat: a variable orifice, varying with differential pressures, operating with oil levels, the body an accurately calibrated gate valve. It integrated for flow, pressure, temperature, and specific gravity. It was installed in many gas manufacturing plants and for large industrial users, also at city gates to measure pipeline natural gas. But these meters required so much service that they were taken off the market. A pipeline fitting was introduced (Robinson) that facilitated orifice changing and promoted utilization of the Westcott type.

While Erie was doing research on orifice meters during the

depression, an enlarged laboratory in Albany concentrated on displacement measurement by tincase meters and on testing apparatus. Improvements and refinements made in tincases in this period were a continuation of American Meter's record of contributions to design and construction. In the impressive list were these:

Redesign of the case and diaphragms for larger bellows and fewer tangent revolutions.

Larger channels for increased rated capacities.

Solid-brass, unobstructed tube-screws.

Stronger operating parts, reducing lost motion.

Three of sixteen station meters housed in one building, and the contrasting size of a Linderman orifice meter

Two-piece valve box cover and frame for access to the valve enclosure.

Adjustable tangent, making adjustments easy.

Valve-seat and crank-bearing casting as an integral part of the valve table, insuring standardized precision.

Straight-reading index, promoting consumer consciousness of the economy of gas use.

Diaphragm dressings suitable for dry natural gas.

In 1930, Albany developed the Bakelite valve cover to eliminate noisy valves and improved the molding compound and treating of this material. Covers were also redesigned to reduce friction. Crank arms were elongated for improved performance. Diaphragm research resulted in leather and dressings much superior to that of a few years before, and development of synthetic diaphragms was in progress.

An exhibit of historic meters going back to 1853 was presented by American Meter at the 1936 A.G.A. convention in Atlantic City. This was American's centennial year, an appropriate time to dramatize evolution.

Progress was still on the wing. The next year witnessed three more pioneering events. American Meter innovated brass die-casting with high-pressure machines turning out unobstructed flanged tube-screws that afforded. gas-tight joints. Brass die-cast cranks and crank stands followed. The Silent Reverse Stop made its appearance—important where back pressure set up in a house line, causing a wrenching stop in reverse tangent travel to twist flag arms from their rods. Formerly a click let the meter run backward for one or two revolutions to absorb back pressure; the new safeguard allowed twenty-five revolutions, eliminating all possibility of strain and damage. It became standard equipment of American meters, as did the Soldered Seal Index Box.

Until now, index box mountings had been made with putty or other plastic and a glazing compound. They were not leakproof, required heavy packing of flag stuffing boxes, hence caused friction and variation from accuracy. A suggestion from the Philadelphia Gas Works prompted American Meter to develop, in cooperation with Corning Glass Works, a permanently gas-tight mounting. This was accomplished by soldering heat-resistant Pyrex glass with an alloy edge directly to the frame of the index box, forming a perfect metallic bond. The Albany factory did the sealing by a process in which flowing solder produced a flawless seam. Gas companies adopted the Soldered Seal Index Box in modernizing their meter equipment.

One phenomenon of the depression was the resurgence of prepayment meters. They had virtually gone out with World War I for divers reasons: their missionary work of bringing gas into homes was done; electricity took over lighting; pilferage was flagrant; bill collectors became less ubiquitous as people began paying by check. The utilities removed prepayment attachments in droves, yet as late as 1920 more than 40 per cent of Tufts' sales was in prepayment meters. The revival in the 1930s was due to the delinquency of many consumers. Instead of shutting off their gas, companies put in prepays while accepting small amounts on old bills, and in some states public service commissions temporarily permitted price wheels at higher rates to work off the debts.

Collections in hard times were a problem for a meter company, too. President Gribbel, an old hand at accepting securities from utilities, obliged present customers in like manner. In one case a gas company owing a considerable sum wanted to place a substantial order for house meters, and he insisted on $300,000 of its bonds.

All the while, natural gas was steadily altering the complexion of the industry at large, spreading over the greater part of the map. Many thousands of miles of transmission lines were built during the depression, delivering heat units to utilities at a cost lower than that of manufactured gas and doubling the capacity of their distribution systems. Changeovers proceeded by the hundreds. Cities as far from the Monroe field in Louisiana as St. Louis in the Middle West, Birmingham and Atlanta in the South, enjoyed the blessing, or a mix of manufactured and natural gas. One of the new pipelines swung from the Texas Panhandle 1250 miles to the Indiana border, connected there to a midstate transmission line, thence to Detroit. Another originating in Texas invaded Minnesota. Where volumes needed to be measured and pressures lowered, American's products were on the job.

What happened in Chicago after conversion was an embarrassment of riches. Consumer demand having fallen, the daily supply that Peoples Gas Light and Coke Company had contracted for became an oversupply. Faced with finding a new mass market, the company plastered billboards around town to advertise house heating. The picture was a contented householder ensconced in an easy chair, saying, "No Winter Worries for Me—I Got Gas Heat."

Peoples received a few letters objecting to the grammar. The order books made pleasanter reading, for with general business conditions improving and factories reopening and buying power restored, Chicagoans turned to gas heating for relief from furnace-tending. Basements became recreation rooms. Wider use of gas always brought a trail of benefits.

Another means of boosting gas consumption arrived with the perfection of Servel's air-cooled gas refrigerator, which involved lower operating costs than those of earlier models. Experimental installations of air conditioners, in homes in several cities, by the A.G.A. committee on industrial gas research, paved the way to marketing this new appliance. Manufacturer members of the association felt they should have a separate organization for more effective distribution of their products and promotion of gas as a fuel. With a benison from the A.G.A. they formed the Association of Gas Appliance and Equipment Manufacturers in 1935 (later renamed Gas Appliance Manufacturers Association). Donald McDonald, one of the incorporators, served as treasurer. So, self-help once again proved, as when the electric light threatened the gas industry, a regenerative force. Gas range sales, for example, rebounded to their 1929 peak.

At this time the use of liquefied petroleum gas was also expanding, and American Meter in conjunction with Phillips Petroleum Company adapted gas meters for accurate measurement of propane and butane in vapor form. Many utility companies were selling bottled gas on a metered basis to patrons living a mile or more from their mains. These rustic residents could have the convenience of automatic refrigerators, as models were marketed that operated on bottled and tank gas.

American Meter's total sales made a sharp advance in 1936 and were on the way to full recovery. John Gribbel did not live to see it. Ill health forced him to retire as president in June; he was elected chairman. In August he died, ending a meter career that had begun in 1883. He had been the last remaining member of the group that organized the consolidated company. The board of directors observed in a memorial resolution, "He was a confirmed optimist."

Frank Payne, the new president, verified the hopes of his predecessor in summing up the company's status, its progress in research and diversification, its strong cash position and capacity for service. In his first annual report to the stockholders Payne wrote:

> Research work in the laboratories at Albany and Erie was continued on the same scale as in recent years. . . . Many new pieces of scientific apparatus were perfected and placed on a production basis. . . .
>
> The American Meter Company through its manufacturing and distributing branches is today a large warehouse in which the interests in manufactured gas, natural gas, petroleum production, refining, and transmission, chemical laboratories and works, oxygen makers and users look for their mechanical equipment to measure and control their products.

President Payne's headquarters were still in Erie. Secretary McDonald, now treasurer also, made his office in New York. His duties as general superintendent were assigned to Norton McKean in Albany.

Griffin Gribbel, Philadelphia factory manager, relinquished the post to his assistant, R. Wallace McClenahan, on becoming vice president. Gribbel served in this capacity briefly, resigning in 1937. McKean succeeded him, but remained in Albany.

The only central seat of power in the company resided in a group of five new directors (notably James G. Leiper, Jr.) who were voting trustees under a trust agreement embracing the Gribbel, Helme, McIlhenny, and Gratz family stockholdings. They went on the board in 1937, joining Payne, McDonald, Gribbel, Arthur E. Norton and Norton McKean (both elected in 1932), and Diehl (1934). Operations continued to be decentralized.

A step in the direction of coordinating certain activities had been taken a few years back when John Van Norden, engaged as assistant secretary in New York, was put in charge of a publication department to handle advertising and publishing, and was made general purchasing agent as well. In a short while, however, the factories resumed their own purchasing. Van Norden then became sales promotion manager.

Arthur F. Benson   Francis W. Benson   A. McW. Wolfe

Through the engineering department, revisions in the design of production equipment and in manufacturing methods, and outlays for replacements and new machine tools, kept the factories at high standards. Erie was designated to make all the brass parts for all. Chief Engineer Diehl played an additional role. Having made a survey of Pacific Meter after William Dickey's departure, he ran that factory from Erie for a few years until Kenneth C. Tomlinson was promoted from assistant to manager.

Selling was still uncoordinated, but interfactory sales went on as of yore. A Philadelphia sales engineer, William G. Hamilton, Jr., who had started with Helme & McIlhenny in its storeroom in 1927, now covered refineries and other customers in the East with special instruments produced by Metric Metal.

The death of Donald McDonald in 1937 marked another break with the past, and yet his impress of fine workmanship was a lasting legacy. He had entered the meter business at the age of seventeen in 1886. It was his life. The offices he held were divided between Payne, treasurer, and Van Norden, secretary.

From where President-Treasurer Payne sat, cooperation between the officers and the men in charge of the factories had reached "a high point of development." It played "an important part in the profitable operations of the Company." He added, "As the senior member of this group of men, I take the greatest pride in what they do and in the way they do it." Sales picked up in

1937 and would have been greater but for an industrial recession in the fall. Payne pointed out that through diversification, sales of products other than the regular meter line amounted to 12.6 per cent of the total.

A factory manager ever since his start in 1891, Payne was especially conscious of the personal element. He wrote:

> Under present-day manufacturing conditions I do not hesitate to say that a most important function of factory managers, superintendents and foremen is to have and to exercise toward the men and women working with them the same spirit of human relationship that they expect in their homes and in their social contacts outside of the factory. The men and women in our factories are persons of intelligence and understanding, and it is a pleasure to record our appreciation of the friendly relationship that exists throughout the organization. Our interests are identical and our responsibilities are mutual.

The quality of concern for the health and safety of employees had probably stemmed from traditions of family management. With all the second- and third-generation scions gone, except Payne, there nevertheless was no depersonalization of attitude. Besides group insurance, in force a good many years, further protection of employees was afforded through coverage for accident, illness, and hospitalization for them and their dependents.

In regard to customers, American Meter's concept was that the sales engineers represented the company to render assistance. "These men are called into conference with customers more and more frequently," Payne noted. "This policy of cooperation engenders a feeling of confidence, creating a relationship much more intimate than simply the relationship of buyer and seller."

—9—

And the Industry Grew

BUSY WAS THE WORD FOR AMERICAN METER COMPANY AS construction of homes and factories in 1939 and the next two years reinvigorated the gas companies. In addition to the deluge of orders for meters and regulators for new installations, parts had to be supplied, repairs made, new meters provided as replacements. Use of LP gas broadened. The oil industry stepped up production, anticipating a war demand. "The entire organization labored strenuously during the greater part of the year" (1941), President Payne wrote, "under exceedingly abnormal conditions of management and manufacturing."

But the company was not too busy to recognize Payne's fiftieth anniversary as manager of the Metric Metal factory. Executives assembled in Erie to pay tribute to the man whose orientation toward natural gas and oil, in contrast to the tincase preoccupations of his late colleagues, had steered American to leadership in hardcase and orifice meters. There was something poetic and prophetic in the fact that Payne was born at Petroleum Center, Pennsylvania, midway between Titusville and Oil City. The Metric works, one of the three largest manufacturer employers in Erie, was American's biggest plant.

Pearl Harbor exploded in the midst of business recovery. For a few months afterward the demand for displacement meters was well sustained, but regulations issued by the War Production Board and the Office of Price Administration hamstrung the gas companies and their suppliers. The utilities were restrained from extending mains, servicing new customers, and even observing their usual schedules of sending in meters for test and repair. Conservation of critical metals for war materials permitted, however, exemption in the case of industrial displacement meters for war production and essential orifice meters and flow controls.

This was the orifice meters' shining hour. They had high priority ratings for the measurement of large volumes of gas and the instrumentation of oil refinery and other petrochemical processes, such as high-octane gasoline, synthetic rubber, and toluene.

Management expected the decline in customary output and hoped to obtain defense jobs fitting in with existing facilities. But American Meter's fabrication work was mainly soldering, the demand for which was scarce. Application to the Small War Plants Corporation, a federal agency, for contracts proved fruitless, because American Meter, taken as a whole, was not deemed a small company. Sheet-metal shops got orders that might have fallen to American.

The difficulty in getting defense work as meter production lagged, except for war housing projects and emergency needs of gas companies, spurred the effort. William Hamilton, then assistant manager of the Philadelphia factory, broke the ice by getting a subcontract for bomb fin assemblies and another for sheet-metal containers. Next, the Boston factory was awarded a contract for casings for hundred-pound chemical bombs, which it subcontracted to Albany for welded steel parts; and Philadelphia received a similar contract. Albany became a prime contractor for both chemical and practice bombs. Boston was also to make burster tubes for these bombs. Erie, being best equipped with machine tools, got fuze orders from Cleveland Ordnance and subcontracts for Air Corps pressure gauges and other aircraft accessories. There was no need to worry about the San Francisco factory because the Marine Corps leased most of it for storage and office space.

The worrisome thing was plant readjustment and acquisition of machinery for the defense jobs when priorities for new machinery were hard to win. American settled for second-hand welders obtained from General Electric, which had to shut down on refrigerators. Conversion to war work was not possible until late in 1942. Francis H. Payne saw only the beginning. He died in November at the age of seventy-four.

Continuing as general superintendent and Albany factory manager, Vice President McKean was elected president with the new year. John Diehl and Arthur Norton became vice presidents. Diehl's post of chief engineer went to Arthur F. Benson, Erie engineer and son of the late Francis Benson. Robert O. Borden assisted Diehl in managing Erie. As defense work multiplied, much of the company's research and engineering talent was devoted to solving production problems.

A firm in Erie that had developed the art of bonding rubber to metal and was making aluminum forgings for airplane engine mounts desperately needed machining. Metric Metal went to its rescue. Manufacture and assembly of engine mounts for planes followed on a large scale. Philadelphia received additional contracts, not only for bomb fins, but also for land mines, waterproof cartridge cases, and mortar containers. The Race Street factory was not ample for all the work; the old Clearfield Street premises were rented back from the new owners. American Meter's defense jobs constituted 62 per cent of its 1943 total, as against 8 per cent the year before, and rose to 71 per cent in 1944.

For "great accomplishment in the production of war equipment" the Army-Navy "E" Award was presented to the employees of the two Philadelphia plants. Ceremonies at Town Hall empha-

Presentation of Army-Navy "E" Award to American Meter Company for excellence in war production achieved by conversion of plant and retraining of workers

sized that the high production goals had been achieved by dint of complete conversion and the retraining of meter makers and other workers unused to the machine and assembly processes involved. A second star on the "E" flag was awarded for continued excellence.

Planning for peace, the American Gas Association undertook a program of research and national advertising to prepare for competition in fuel utilization. The company contributed to the fund, through the Association of Gas Appliance and Equipment Manufacturers, in accordance with its policy to support projects for industry advancement. "They protect the future welfare of our customers on a nationwide basis, with resulting benefit to equipment manufacturers," said McKean. In its own postwar planning, American Meter formed two groups of researchers, one to make a market survey and determine how many meters the customers would require. The other, an engineering development group for product improvement, would benefit by wartime experience gained in working with new materials, new machine tools and manufacturing methods.

This was the prelude. Profound organizational changes were afoot, apart from a decision to replace the outmoded Race Street factory as soon as possible and a resolution to coordinate sales activities in Philadelphia after the war. New thinking was applied to the prospects for company growth.

The chief architect of change was Thomas A. Bracken, Jr., vice president and trust officer of the Real Estate Bank and Trust Company of Philadelphia, as fiduciary for the stockholding families under the trust agreement. He was elected a director in 1942. Bracken enlisted John B. Klumpp, an oustanding gas utility engineer and former A.G.A. president, former chairman of the Philadelphia Gas Commission, now a consultant. Klumpp became a director of American Meter in 1943. Bracken wanted the board to engage him for special studies, to make recommendations regarding operations, and this was done with the supportive voice of James G. Leiper, Jr., a Philadelphia attorney, one of the group of directors who had come in under the trusteeship.

After V-J Day in 1945 the board adopted the recommendation of Bracken, Leiper, and Klumpp to establish an operating committee which would meet monthly and thresh out ideas on sales, production, labor relations, engineering, and research for the

Wm. G. Hamilton, Jr.   C. Benson Dushane, Jr.   John W. Ostler

common good of the several factories. McKean was chairman of the committee. Fellow members were Diehl and Benson of Erie, Hamilton (now manager) of Philadelphia, McClenahan (on his return from military service), Wolfe of Boston, and Van Norden in the New York office. Their meetings generated closer understanding of mutual problems.

Meanwhile, Klumpp made his studies of the over-all company picture and turned in reports. The scattered functions of management were due for centralization. The company would be in a much stronger position, for example, if it had control of all financial matters at one point, also if all customers' purchase orders came to a single point for a better estimate of the manufacturing load and inventory requirements. Indeed, Bracken and Leiper reasoned in executive committee councils that the company would have greater possibility of growth and better administration if all officers were in one location and the top functions centered there. This would come in time.

A major step in the direction of centralizing functions was taken with the creation of new positions effective at the beginning of 1947. Instead of having a general superintendent, a manager of production was named, Arthur Benson. For the first time American Meter had a salesmanager, William G. Hamilton, Jr. R. W. McClenahan became director of purchases. All three were made vice presidents (McClenahan resigned after a few months). In the sales set-up C. Benson Dushane, Jr., in charge of the Midwest division since 1941 and former president of the Midwest Gas Association, was Chicago district manager. Other district managers were Alexander McW. Wolfe, Boston; James J. Cooney, Albany; Kenneth C. Tomlinson, Pacific Coast; John Van Norden, New York, with Alexander B. Cloud as his assistant. Temporary quarters for central control were taken in Philadelphia on North Broad Street.

Griffin Gribbel had died in December 1946. Almost forty years before, he had followed in his father's footsteps for a life in the meter business. A director for the past ten years, he was the last member of the board to be closely tied by family to an American Meter plant. The changeover from autonomous factory functioning almost coincided with his death.

When war production declined in 1945 (it made up 53 per cent of the year's sales), it left the company facing a huge backlog of meter orders and stumbling blocks to reconversion. Materials were in short supply, manpower in the industries on which the company relied was also insufficient, deliveries of new machinery were delayed. Nor were enough meter-maker workers available who were trained to make a quality product. Some utilities had to put in gas services without meters.

The Albany factory, least affected, produced more tincase meters in 1945 than Philadelphia and Boston combined. To make the best of the difficult situation in Philadelphia, Hamilton, while manager, worked out a line assembly. It was the first of its kind and did so well that the other factories adopted it. While the product shortage prevailed, gas operators in the field wanted to know how to do more with equipment on hand; Benson offered help and was in great demand as an instructor and speaker.

Planned increase of production received further setbacks in 1946. Tinplate was drastically curtailed by government priorities benefiting the food-packing program. An upset leather market limited the quantity of sheepskins for diaphragms. Major strikes tied up the steel and coal industries, causing repercussions. Pig iron and gray iron castings and other basic items fell far below requirements. In sum, the output of meters failed to come up even to the plants' normal level of capacity.

Untried substitutes for standard construction were avoided. It meant a sacrifice of immediate sales, but the temporary advantage would not be worth while if it impaired reputation for performance. In the search for acceptable materials, cast-aluminum bodies augmented the supply of some sizes of ironcases and regulators. Orders for these were filled in Erie. Soon after, President McKean reported to the board on the desirability of buying molds for a die-cast aluminum meter, equivalent to a 5B ironcase, to be ready for a market demand that might develop.

A research committee was formed for aggressive efforts to insure American Meter's prominence in its specialized field. Besides capital expenditures to expand the Erie and Albany laboratories, the budget for research was more than tripled, enabling the staff to undertake more thorough and comprehensive studies and analyses of new proposals. High on the list stood redesign and modernization of prewar products and the testing of process techniques.

The outlay for new machinery to give manufacturing the benefit of technological advances was nearly half a million dollars in 1947, an additional quarter-million in 1948. Structural changes in the factories and the modern equipment helped keep the company somewhat abreast of insistent demand. Purchase of the inventory and physical assets of Lambert Meter Company, a fair-sized manufacturer of tincase meters in Brooklyn, afforded some relief of the dire shortage of low-pressure meters. In San Francisco, Pacific Meter Works was rejuvenated. The factory was sold as unsuitable for current needs and a single-story structure was built on Tennessee Street that went a long way toward catching up with the phenomenally fast growth of the Pacific Coast area.

Canadian Meter Company had a backlog of its own to work off and a strong postwar call for LP meters. Erie helped by shipping parts for assembly. As rumors of a Trans-Canada natural-gas transmission system wafted across the Dominion, this largest meter factory in the country was remodeled for increased production after having expanded its original size several times. Now there were prospects of a brand-new plant for the Maple Leaf division.

American Meter's sales mounted in the first full year of peacetime production. Although they had been greater at the height of the war, defense work had yielded a small margin of profit. The current figure represented in part higher prices resulting from higher manufacturing costs; but larger volume and operational efficiency held prices from rising proportionately. Even so, certain items were limited to two-thirds of plant capacity, because sufficient materials were still unavailable. The demand kept on. The factories really hit their stride in 1948.

The pent-up forces behind the demand were by no means spent. Gas as fuel had taught industries during the war that it was the ideal fuel, giving perfect heat control for vulcanizing tires, hardening and tempering alloy steel, melting glass and metals, smoking meat, pasteurizing, and much, much else. Gas did not tie up money in fuel investment. It eliminated the need for fuel storage space and for ash removal, and eliminated smoke. Industries wanted gas and more of it.

In homes, improved gas ranges ousted old models, improved automatic water heaters too gave greater consumer satisfaction, and gas-fired washing machines, dryers, and ironers left the laundry unaffected by weather. Space heaters supplanted coal furnaces, most of which wasted most of the coal. A flip colloquial expression of approval went the rounds: "Now you're cooking with gas!"

More dwellings in the Chicago area had converted to house heating by gas than anywhere else. Peoples' former oversupply of Texas gas was fully consumed. The waiting list of homeowners was even larger than the number who were smiling like the man in the billposter and whose supply had to be protected. Once the scarcity of steel pipe subsided, a second pipeline paralleling the first from the Panhandle was completed for a combined daily delivery of 500 million cubic feet. No sooner was that done than a third line was planned to come from the Texas Gulf Coast. American Meter measured all of this gas.

Until Chicago's third line came in, the largest pipeline for transmission of natural gas was the war-emergency construction by Tennessee Gas Transmission Company to furnish fuel for the highly industrialized Appalachian region. This extended 1265 miles from Nueces County, Texas, to West Virginia, using pipe of twenty-four-inch diameter. It might have been called Big Inch, but that name already belonged to an oil pipeline.

Big Inch was a cooperative project of oil companies to beat the Nazi submarine menace that sank tankers off the Atlantic Coast. There was need also to overcome congestion of other forms of transportation to the East. Under contract to the Defense

Plant Corporation the companies built two gigantic pipelines. One carried crude oil from Longview in eastern Texas by twenty-four-inch pipe to Phoenixville, Pennsylvania, and by twenty-inch pipe from there to Linden, New Jersey (1340 miles total), for delivery to nearby refineries; a branch line from Phoenixville went to refineries in the Philadelphia area. The other construction, called Little Big Inch, brought gasoline and other oil products to Linden in twenty-inch pipe 1475 miles from Beaumont and Houston.

These two pipelines were turned over to the War Assets Administration after the war. For an emergency supply to Appalachian industries in the winter of 1945, Tennessee Gas Transmission converted Big Inch to a gas carrier on a short-term lease. Something else was cooking. Holley Poe, a former gas company manager in the Southwest, helped organize Texas Eastern Transmission Corporation and gave a talk before the Society of Gas Lighting on "Proposed Plans for the Use of Big and Little Big Inch Pipelines." He predicted that natural gas would be brought to New York City.

The plans and realizations of natural-gas interests were, in the Hollywood phrase, simply stupendous. In 1947 Texas Eastern bought Big Inch and Little Big Inch from the government for more than $143,000,000 and started installing gas compressor stations. The same year saw completion of Biggest Inch from the

American Meter's old factory in Race Street, Philadelphia

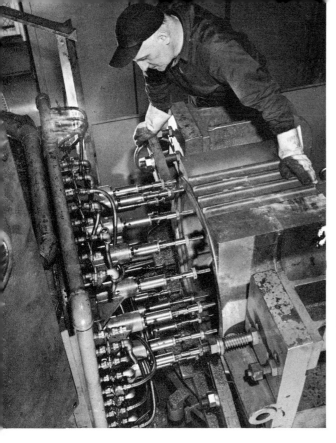

Multiple automatic drilling
and tapping a 500 B meter

Permian basin in Texas to Southern California, with a final link
of thirty-inch pipe. The Federal Power Commission authorized
many new pipelines and extensions—increased supplies to Kansas
City, St. Louis, Detroit, Minneapolis; a new line to Denver; for
Tennessee Gas, an extension from West Virginia to Albany and
Boston. Transcontinental Gas Pipe Line Corporation was authorized to build from Hidalgo County, Texas, to Philadelphia and
through New Jersey to New York. In 1949 came the start of
Super-Inch, to connect the El Paso network to P. G. and E. with
thirty-four-inch pipe, an economy size. Columbia Gas System
received approval to serve Baltimore. And Big Inch brought natural gas to the New York & Richmond Gas Company in Staten
Island.

Manhattan, Brooklyn, New England—more millions of consumers would soon be getting their gas from the fabulous Southwest. Production of manufactured gas was already on the decline.
It slipped from a record 597 billion cubic feet in 1947, when the
figure for natural-gas consumption was 4.4 trillion.

Broad opportunities opened up for American Meter products

by virtue of this great expansion of natural-gas distribution. "It presents a challenge, of which our sales and engineering departments are aware," said McKean.

The organization was becoming streamlined. By arrangement with the Real Estate Bank and Trust Company the services of Director Bracken as treasurer were afforded without salary. Centralized accounting, purchasing, sales, and inventory control heightened efficiency. Named controller was Alexander McBeath, formerly resident controller in Erie. The Race Street plant was rearranged to provide space for the central accounting office and other activities conducted from the Broad Street office. Following purchase of the minority interest in Reliance Regulator Corporation from the Thompson estate, Reliance was a wholly owned subsidiary, then was dissolved as a corporation and integrated with American Meter as a division.

The company spent an additional $700,000 for machinery, equipment, and plant in 1949 and 1950 to lower the cost of products and improve their performance. A new feature was continuous-machining, follow-through equipment in which more

A modern installation: 500 B meter with Base Volume Index, other instruments, and Regulators

than a hundred production tools milled, drilled, and tapped meter bodies held rigidly in moving fixtures. This made possible undeviating accuracy in the positioning of subassemblies. Perhaps the greatest technical improvement was self-lubricating, porous bronze bearings for least wear and longest life.

Research came through with the development of the Series A-88 line of instruments, including pneumatic, for precision transmission and control in continuous processing by measuring flow, pressure, liquid level, and other variables. The Telecounter was also new—an electrically operated device for remote reading of integrated gas quantities, transmitting the information over telephone wires to distant dispatchers. Many improvements were made in the design of positive displacement meters and LP-gas equipment.

The administration line-up changed in 1950. McKean resigned as president for reasons of health, but remained as a director. The executive committee invited Diehl to serve—a rare honor for a man of science. Diehl was willing if he could have Hamilton aid him in the general duties. Another change was in Benson's title to vice president in charge of engineering, management of all production going to Archie E. Weingard, who subsequently became vice president of production. The company lost the versatile services of John Van Norden; on his death, Sophia L. Blume, who had assisted him and Donald McDonald before him in New York, was elected secretary.

Hamilton worked with Diehl on sales organization, labor, manufacturing, and a wide range of matters. After Diehl suffered a stroke while riding to a convention, his aide-de-camp reported directly to the executive committee.

A place for Hamilton was made on the board of directors in 1951. He became president, Diehl chairman. Benson Dushane was named vice president of sales. In the new array of vice presidents were Donald C. Wiley, for research, and D. Clark Struble, for purchasing. Re-elected to this rank was Arthur E. Norton, whose fifty years with American had recently been commemorated, and whose associate, Alexander Wolfe, was also a v.p. A new secretary was elected, William B. Ashby; he had started with the company in 1940 in training as a sales engineer.

At last the administration was largely concentrated in Philadelphia. Treasurer Bracken stayed close at hand as advisor to the officers on financial and policy matters with his intimate knowledge of the company's affairs. Neither he nor Director Leiper skipped a single meeting of the board or the executive committee.

American Meter was launched on a decade of extraordinary growth during which more than $9,000,000 would be expended in capital investment.

A lamplighter as of yore: one of the last gas lampposts on Baltimore streets, removed in the 1950s

—10—

Organized for Growth

ON A COLD DAY IN JANUARY 1951 THE PRESIDENT OF TRANSCONTI-
nental Gas Pipe Line Corporation turned a valve at a point in
Manhattan where a pipeline from Texas crossed the Hudson
River. The flow to a Consolidated Edison meter station initiated
the changeover from manufactured gas in the metropolitan area.
This line, using American Meter orifice meters, delivered more
than 109 billion cubic feet of natural gas to consumers in the
broader New York-New Jersey-Philadelphia region during the
first year, eventually almost tripling the annual figure with more
than half a million homes converted to gas heating.

A pipeline across Massachusetts was completed in 1951 by
Northeastern Gas Transmission Company for service to a large
part of New England. Other systems greatly increased their mile-
age and capacity, and utility companies augmented their supplies for consumers old and new. The requirements of the Boston
Gas Company alone grew to a hundred million cubic feet a day.

As completion of the new pipelines increased the demand for
gas, it increased the demand for American Meter products. Re-
organization of factory facilities became essential. Certainly,
Philadelphia needed a modern plant, away from downtown traffic
on Race Street, though the present building might be remodeled
for general offices; the new factory must be somewhere in the
city area in order to retain the skilled personnel. In the open
country of suburban Somerton, a tract of twelve and a half acres
was purchased—plenty of room to spread. Plans called for a one-
story structure to house tincase meter production and engineering
and research centers, with an adjoining administration building.

An exceptionally strong demand arose for ironcases. Erie's
large factory was not large enough, not even with regulators
moved out to leased quarters. Besides, savings in freight costs

Texas natural gas for New York City: welding the final section of a mile-long crossing of the Hudson River in 1950 to the metering station in Manhattan

could be realized if ironcases for the Southwest and West were produced nearer these markets. Following a decision to establish such a resource in the Middle West, Treasurer Bracken and Arthur Benson conferred with civic leaders of Nebraska City, Nebraska, on cooperation in building a plant in this community on the Missouri River and arranged the financing. Erie discontinued tin meters (had stopped making Tobeys in 1942) and put in progress-through machines for small iron meters and additional machine tools for large-size cast-iron meters.

Another way to improve service to customers was to open an assembly plant for orifice meters and instruments in Dallas. This took only a few months, so it was the first of the new facilities.

California's rate growth, outpacing the San Francisco factory, dictated realignment of West Coast production. Arthur Benson made a survey in the neighborhood of Los Angeles with the result that twenty-one acres were acquired at Fullerton, south of Los Angeles. Here was a good place to consolidated San Francisco and Los Angeles activities in a spacious factory that could also accommodate the Reliance Regulator division for a greater output. A warehouse in San Francisco would take care of Northern California's quick needs.

Nor was this the last of immediate construction projects. Intensified action in the oil and natural-gas fields of Alberta prompted Canadian Meter Company to provide a service center and warehouse in Edmonton in 1953.

The same year, the Nebraska City plant (60,000 square feet) opened according to plan, but its destiny was diverted. Aluminumcase meters were winning favor among utilities. Where formerly accepted as a substitute when iron castings were scarce, aluminum had meter setters on its side to influence choice. They naturally preferred the fifteen pounds of a 5B aluminumcase to the thirty-five pounds of its iron counterpart. Of one-piece die-casting, the new type had high resistance to impact damage and ample capacity for household heating loads. It was introduced in 1954, made both in Erie and in Nebraska City. Before long the latter plant was confining itself to domestic aluminum meters, not simply for its originally allotted territory but for the entire country.

Just as tincases were declining in popularity, yielding in turn to iron and aluminum, so small-size ironcases were on the wane.

Industrial sizes in iron, however, remained an Erie specialty. As aluminumcases of large capacity found appeal for industrial use, Erie designed and produced these too.

Tincases faced still another rival—a fresh concept of meter life —even as the Fullerton and Somerton plants were on the drawing board. If a meter company was basically conservative, it also had to be resilient. American Meter wrestled with the concept and readjusted itself.

It all arose from a request from Consolidated Edison of New York for a disposable meter. That is, one that could be retired rather than repaired after a reasonable period, thereby saving the expense of maintenance (often 70 per cent of the original cost). The price must be low enough to warrant discard. This was astute thinking, but Con Edison also made two specifications to clarify its goal: higher working pressure and lower capacity (60 to 75 c.f.) for apartment dwellers and other domestic users having no space heating load.

Benson and his Erie staff worked on the means of getting higher pressure without having to go to the expense of a hardcase. The solution was one of his last contributions. American Meter's standard tin meter was put in a welded case for pressure up to five pounds per square inch. The W-60 model, forerunner of W-75 and a "W" series of higher capacities, required 22 per cent fewer parts than the tincase; many assembly operations were automatic.

The economy of welded meters foretokened the disappearance of Con Edison's repair shop. As changeovers to natural gas proceeded in heavily populated Manhattan and The Bronx, that company placed large orders for W-60s. They could be bought for almost the same amount it would cost to repair older and larger meters on the system. In Southern California, top management of the utilities welcomed the new concept and asked American Meter to produce a 5-lt. welded.

Millions of household meters throughout the country were more than twenty-five years old. Replacements were due and overdue. Any lessening of the spread between the cost of repair and the price of a new meter was tempting enough to speed the rate of condemnation. The 5-lt. welded seemed bound to become the standard and supplant tincases of the 5B size with its heavier-gauge material and its greater safety factor in not being hand-soldered. Therefore Hamilton approached his board of directors for an authorization to tool up a 5-lt. welded line; the equipment, jigs, dies, and fixtures were to go mainly to the two factories opening in 1955, Fullerton and Somerton. The money was granted.

Companion of the welded meter in this evolutionary change was a synthetic diaphragm. The quest for a suitable substitute for oiled leather had been going on in the Albany laboratory intensively in the past thirty years, more so as the problem of obtaining satisfactory leather became more difficult. Many cotton fabrics coated with synthetic rubber, tested under severe conditions, were found wanting in one or more of the necessary characteristics. American Meter was reluctant to guarantee any of the proposed materials. Albany made diaphragms from fabrics of various manufacturers and kept gathering performance data and acting as a clearing house for information as customers took more than an academic interest. Finally, Albany embarked on a program that involved two years of laboratory tests and the collaboration of gas companies in widespread field tests to find the right fabric and coating formulation that would resist any combination of active hydrocarbons in any kind of gas, in any city.

When American Meter felt it had a proven, acceptable product, the manufacture of Duramic Diaphragms began in 1954, Albany molding them from duPont material. The name suggested durability. Duramic was a declaration of independence from the ancient reign of sheepskin with a much cheaper diaphragm that was also better suited to the modern age of natural gas.

Research meant as much to the company in terms of future growth as the brick and concrete and physical equipment of the new plants. The creative work of Arthur F. Benson in Erie alongside John Diehl for twenty-three years, bringing products important to the company's success, had come to an end in 1953. Fortunately, Benson had insisted on thorough training of his associates, thereby forming a research and development team capable of carrying the work forward.

One of Diehl's and Benson's protégés was Hilding V. Beck, former member of the engineering faculty of the University of Oklahoma and an authority on orifice meter measurement. Beck, who had given the Southwestern Gas Measurement Short Course at the university, associated himself with Westcott & Greis in 1936 and joined the Erie staff in 1937. After Benson's death, Donald

A typical modern American Meter plant: at Fullerton, California

Wiley filled the dual post of vice president of engineering and research and Beck was appointed chief engineer. Diehl served a while as vice president and consulting research engineer. Beck later became vice president of engineering.

Time brought a decided change in the complexion of the board of directors. John Diehl had dropped out because of difficulty in attending meetings, Arthur Norton also for reasons of health, and John Klumpp died in 1955. Woodward W. Corkran, a director since 1937, resigned. The four new members were Philadelphians who applied their outside manufacturing experience: Herbert J. Adair, president of Artloom Carpet Company; Ralph Earle, vice president of South Chester Tube Company; Albert J. Nesbitt, president of John J. Nesbitt, Inc.; and James H. Carmine, president of Philco Corporation.

In the course of plant modernization, during the first six years of the decade more than half of the factory facilities had been replaced. Erie, with its 192,300 square feet of floor area, remained the largest unit. The Albany factory was no longer needed; its waning tin meter requirements were divided between Philadelphia and Boston, its production of laboratory gas-testing apparatus transferred to Erie, so that only diaphragms were left (temporarily). The books closed on Albany and its ancient lineage in 1957. Boston was retained chiefly for tin meter repairs.

For diaphragm production the company acquired a small firm

that employed people who had done some of the first development work on synthetics—Permoflex Rubber Products, Inc., in Farmingdale, Long Island, New York—and in 1957 built a fair-sized plant (30,100 square feet) at Wyalusing in the northern part of Pennsylvania.

Fullerton, starting with 60,000 square feet, responded to the completion of pipelines into the Pacific Northwest, the last big geographical area of the country opened up to natural gas. An addition taking in regulator manufacture from Alhambra made this plant American Meter's second largest (114,000 square feet total). George W. Stevenson, a newcomer in 1928, had climbed the ladder to the rung of manager (soon vice president) of West Coast operations.

The Somerton plant was third largest with 77,400 square feet. When the general office building was ready for occupancy in the spring of 1956 (bringing over-all floorspace to 110,000 square feet), engineering, research, manufacturing, and industrial relations departments were transferred there from Erie, under one roof with the sales department, accounting, and administration. Experimentation was concentrated in a laboratory built in Huntingdon Valley near the Philadelphia headquarters.

Also new in 1956 was a permanent site for the Texas instrument assembly unit after four years in leased space in Dallas. It was built (20,000 square feet) in Garland, near Dallas, on a plot of eleven acres.

Canada shared in new construction. Anticipating strong stimulus from natural gas, Canadian Meter Company acquired thirteen acres in Milton, Ontario, and moved from Hamilton into a plant providing 35,000 square feet for aluminum and ironcase meters, later also for assembly of orifice meters and manufacture of regulators. The Pacific Northwest Pipe Line system brought gas from the San Juan basin of New Mexico to the Canadian border. Vancouver received it, also supplies from the Peace River region of British Columbia and Alberta. Trans-Canada Pipe Lines started building 2,250 miles across the continent with thirty-six-inch pipe and delivered Peace River gas to Toronto and Montreal and communities on the way. For John W. Ostler, a clerk in John McNary's office in 1937, the progress of the Canadian subsidiary was like a personal triumph. He had advanced to assistant man-

Natural gas pipelines built across mountains, prairie, and desert: *(top)* 30-in.-diameter pipe over rocky terrain in Arizona; *(middle)* through farmland in western Canada; *(bottom)* laying a line from New Mexico to California

Offshore Louisiana, a major source
natural gas reserves: concrete-coat
pipe sent from the mainland to t
bottom of the Gulf of Mexico for
new supply

ager, to general manager and treasurer, and in 1957 became president and general manager.

All the new plant facilities were built and equipped by American Meter without having to resort to outside financing. The wherewithal had come through prudent management, efficient operation, and steadily rising sales.

Although the cycle of plant construction had ended, except for the Fullerton addition and others in Nebraska City and Milton, another force was at work for company expansion. Its name was diversification.

Company policy had determined that the line of expansion should preferably be in the general field of measurement. The first step was the purchase in 1954 of a two-thirds interest in the Philadelphia Pump & Machinery Company, makers of controlled-capacity proportioning pumps. This too was metering. The pumps were used principally in water treating, whereby chemicals were added in direct proportion to flow; also in the petroleum industry for expensive additives and in chemical processes. After acquiring the remaining outstanding stock in 1957, the parent company merged the subsidiary as its pump division.

Another kind of pump came through a different acquisition. But preceding this, American Meter learned that a highly estimable firm making household water meters was up for sale, its two major and elderly stockholders wishing to retire. Five million dollars would buy it. Oddly enough, while American's corporate charter in 1910 had specified "articles pertaining to gas and water works," only during the past five years had American studied the manufacture of water meters.

Here was a field of very rapid growth. While the gas industry was forecast to grow at a rate comparable to that of the nation, *every* dwelling in the land required water. Buffalo Meter Company sold a complete range of sizes to municipal and private water companies. American acquired the entire outstanding stock and a 99,000-square-foot plant in Buffalo, New York, in 1958 on a loan from The Equitable Life Assurance Society of the United States. The personnel was retained. The plus factor was that Buffalo meters were made in various metals, in diameters from five-eighths of an inch to six inches, to measure molasses, sugar syrup, acids—any flowing liquid in an industrial process.

In the measurement of petroleum products, American's orifice-type flow meters, flow controllers, and temperature and pressure instruments did not encompass all the requirements of the petroleum industry. Displacement meters were also needed. Granberg Corporation, of Oakland, California, made these for bulk plants, refineries, and oil pipeline companies, and transfer pumps for dispensing from oil tank trucks. Granberg's outstanding stock and factory (31,000 square feet in three buildings) were obtained in exchange for shares of American Meter stock in 1959.

Working with American's research department, Buffalo and Granberg developed automated measuring equipment. Electri-volume meters gave Buffalo Meter customers pushbutton automation for all types of liquid processing applications. Granberg afforded economy with an Accounta/Key system whereby tank trucks could load petroleum products at unattended bulk plants around the clock; an operator's personal key, a liquid meter, and electronic impulses performed the service, and a digital readout resulted.

American's pump division also developed a novel control mechanism. It permitted wide adjustment of chemical feed pumps without interruption of operations. Air-operated metering pumps accurately proportioned, blended, and dispensed multi-component mixes, such as reactive liquid resins.

Instruments were a fascinating branch of American Meter research. One of the fruits was a force amplifier which actuated devices by accepting small input forces from delicate instruments and producing an output motion up to a thousand times greater. Another spectacular development was the Gasclok, a gas-driven unit for operating instruments at locations remote from other power sources. It delivered more than twenty times the torque of conventional spring-wound mechanisms and provided continuous timing accuracy.

Speaking of measurement engineering feats and customers' special needs, a BTU Meter simplified accounting of individual users of central air conditioning. This utilized an integrating device developed by American for other products of the company. Multiplying a water meter reading by a temperature differential factor, the BTU Meter recorded the heat units removed from specific areas.

A growing use of American products was in automatic measurement of gas flowing to groups of well-pumps, and of consumption at each well-pump, in the irrigation of farmlands in the Southwest, with Reliance Regulators maintaining the required pressures. Customers' needs varied and many were complex. The company added engineers to its sales organization to design economical systems and supervise installation. New gas distribution networks in particular called forth their talents, such as one that served twenty-four communities and covered 300 miles, a vibration-proof Telecounter controlling all critical variables from a central location.

Besides Dri-flo orifice meters used as flowmeters by pipeline and utility companies, Granco (Granberg) turbine meters for pipeline and transfer service, and Table Chart Integrators giving fast, precise accounting (they integrated both round and strip charts), the company sought many other ways to facilitate the work of the gigantic natural-gas industry. Gas Lift Meters, employed with orifice-type meters, measured and recorded intermittent flows of gas into wells during pressurizing. Pressure boosters of two types, both automatic, were among these developments.

The industry had reached the point where it supplied nearly one-third of the nation's fuel energy. Despite sharply rising consumption, new recoverable natural-gas reserves kept exceeding each year the sales of that year. Discoveries, new drilling methods bringing in wells that had been supposed depleted, and the tapping of offshore reserves in Gulf Coast tidewater areas made the future secure. Thousands of underground storage wells were maintained over the country, enabling gas to be piped from the source in summer and delivered for the higher load of house heating in winter.

The gas appliance industry continued to grow with the lengthening pipelines and the radiating service lines that accompanied the population trend to the suburbs. New types of water heaters, incinerators, clothes dryers, and thermostatically controlled top burners on gas ranges attested to the ingenuity of the manufacturers. Home air conditioners operated by gas were encouraged by the gas-and-electric utilities as a means of balancing winter peaks and taking some of the summer load off the electric system. Industrial and commercial appliances in many instances were tailored to suit the situations.

American brought out Reliance house regulators in a number

of models to control pressure to domestic appliances, as well as industrial regulators and other large sizes for control at high and low pressures in distribution systems. A compact regulator for the home was one of the new products.

Economy—the urgent idea in American Meter's slogan, "Sustained Accuracy at a Lower Cost"—motivated research. While working on electronic devices, pulse generators, and digital techniques of measurement, the researchers did not seek to revolutionize gas meters but to modernize the meter line for competitive economies. Improved materials, bigger bearings, a smaller meter, lower cost per pound—these were the objectives. A smaller package. Less weight. But with sustained accuracy.

These considerations governed the design of new aluminum and welded meters. The AL-425, taking big loads, weighed only eighteen pounds. The AL-800 was also of compact design. The AL-250 operated at only seven revolutions per cubic foot instead of the conventional nine and provided long life. There were also smaller sizes for natural gas and LP-gas, such as the AL-110 for homes using LP-gas for space heating. The line of welded meters was also extended, including WC-45 for light-load applications of LP-gas. At the same time, American developed the Automatic Prover for testing positive displacement meters at a saving of time and labor in utilities' meter shops.

Still prompted by the industry's needs, research developed the Temperature Compensator. This was incorporated in aluminumcases to permit a utility to set domestic meters outdoors in northern climates for precise measurement under varying temperatures. It provided the same advantages as curb meters in Florida and California, saving reading time and responsibility for service piping. And in further thinking along these lines, the laboratory evolved Teleread, an electronic device to be plugged in on the outside of a house for a reading—no need to ring doorbells. Good for water meters, Teleread was expected to be good also for gas meters.

In a service business like American's, products were not the sole concern. Technical education of newcomers in the industry and of veterans wanting to catch up with recent advances was a normal function. Meter schools for trainees had started at Norman, Oklahoma, in 1924 and were held in other college centers, the company participating by sending lecturers. American also made loans or gifts of equipment to engineering schools and contributed to their building funds. Through the efforts of E. S. Dickey in cooperation with the Southern Gas Association, a chair of gas engineering was established at The Johns Hopkins University. At the request of customers an industry school convened in Dallas (1954 and thereafter once a year or oftener) for technical graduates and people with fifteen or more years of instrument experience; under Beck's direction they covered instrument theory and applications and exchanged ideas. The publishing activity initiated by Frank Payne continued. A new revision of *Handbook E-4* was issued under the title *Displacement Gas Meters.*

At the other end of the service spectrum, American Meter carried information to the public. Vice President Benson Dushane believed the company should help stimulate consumer use of gas, consequently he placed a series of institutional advertisements in *The Saturday Evening Post, Life,* and *Time* (1953-55) with such headlines as "How Gas Packs *Your* Home With Comfort" and "Gas Is Popular," "Gas Is Modern." The running theme was, "When you build, buy or remodel, be sure your home is modern with gas." President William Hamilton proposed at a meeting of the Gas Appliance Manufacturers Association that other suppliers to the industry help shoulder the cost of an enlarged program. This was done: a separate permanent group, the Gas Equipment Manufacturers Association, was formed in New York to carry on a cooperative campaign in popular magazines and other media.

American Meter desired that homage be paid to men in the industry who made outstanding contributions to the science and art of distribution. An annual award in the form of a plaque, a wristwatch, and a $1000 check would be underwritten by the company but administered by the A.G.A. and called the A.G.A. Distribution Achievement Award. Selections by an association committee were subject to review by the executive committee of the A.G.A. board of directors. First to win the honor (1952) was Frank J. Hall of Michigan Consolidated Gas Company, Detroit, with special recognition of his "prominent part in development of the lightweight service trencher." In the ensuing years the high standards of selection observed by the jury established the stature of the award as a "Nobel Prize" for distribution. The

At the New York Stock Exchange, the day of the listing: William B. Ashby, Dante E. Broggi, C. Benson Dushane, Jr., William G. Hamilton, Jr., Edward G. Gray (executive vice president of the Exchange), Alexander McBeath

most recent recipient (1961) was Anthony H. Cramer of Michigan Consolidated Gas Company for his activities in the development of codes for safety in the gas industry.*

On the fiscal side of American's historical ledger, the year 1960 ended with consolidated net sales close to $41,000,000. The past decade of factory modernization and expansion, of research effort, product improvement and innovation, of property acquisitions and integration (including absorption of Westcott & Greis into the parent body) and perhaps above all, centralized administration, had demonstrated the company's vitality. At the end of 1960 the net worth of the company was almost double the amount

---

* Recipients of the A.G.A. Distribution Achievement Award in the intervening years were: John E. Overbeck, Columbia Gas System Service Corporation, Columbus, Ohio (1953); Fred H. Bunnell, Consumers Power Company, Jackson, Michigan (1954); George K. Bachmann, Public Service Electric and Gas Company, Newark, New Jersey (1955); Walter C. Peters, Northern States Power Company, Minneapolis, Minnesota (1956); Sidney E. Trouard, New Orleans Public Service, Inc., New Orleans, Louisiana (1957); Frederick G. Sandstrom, Consolidated Edison Company of New York, Inc., New York (1958); E. F. Trunk, Laclede Gas Company, St. Louis, Missouri (1959); C. P. Xenis, Consolidated Edison Company of New York, Inc. (1960).

in 1950 and adequate dividends had been paid out of the earnings during this period. American Meter stock was admitted to trading on the New York Stock Exchange in March 1961.

Of the thirty million gas meters in service in the United States, more than half were manufactured by American. Canadian Meter was sharing (by aiding) the remarkable industrial progress of the Dominion and prepared to handle Granberg petroleum metering equipment for its market. Granberg and Buffalo Meter were winning new and helping old friends with their automated products. Permoflex, improving synthetic diaphragms, continued as the parent company's source of supply and as a source for utilities in their meter maintenance.

American looked to further expansion within the general field of measurement with new products suitable for its manufacturing and marketing facilities and to further diversification by acquiring going businesses in comparable areas.

The board of directors approached the future with the support of two new members. Chester S. Crawford, president of Whitehall Cement Manufacturing Company, of Philadelphia, joined in 1960 after the death of James A. McCurdy, a director since 1937. Dante E. Broggi, former president of Neptune Meter Company, who had served American as a consultant in the negotiations with Buffalo Meter and subsequently became a vice president of American in charge of the subsidiary, was elected a director in 1961.

For the employees of American Meter, numbering more than two thousand, the outlook was continued harmony with management and opportunities for personal growth. The company followed a policy of building from within. Many of the personnel had never worked for any firm but American and were members of the Twenty-five-year Service Guild in their plant. Many were third- and fourth-generation employees.

Nobody laid claim to being a descendant of a fellow-worker of Samuel Down in 1836, or he would have been snatched by Douglas R. Kramer, the advertising manager, as a symbol for American Meter's 125th anniversary in 1961. The company had to content itself with pride in its long history and present eminence.

The anniversary year opened with full confidence that the demands for measurement engineering would bring new challenge and solutions. A tribute paid to John C. Diehl by the Natural Gasoline Association of America was a reminder of achievement. In bestowing the Hanlon Award, highest honor in the gas processing industry, the association cited Diehl for his "many significant contributions."

> He not only made discoveries of great value to the industry, but he recognized the need of industry for them and he had the ability to explain his ideas in written texts so that they could be applied in the field. A whole generation of measurement men, the gas industry, and the gas processing industry owe this man a vote of thanks and gratitude for his monumental aid in making their operations easier and much more accurate.

The anniversary year also brought American Rotary Meters into the line of products under a selling arrangement with the Roots-Connersville Blower Division of Dresser Industries. They were used as station meters for manufactured-gas plants in place of wet meters and for industrial needs. They still have a place on loads between positive-displacement diaphragm meters and orifice meters. Orifice meters, however, are generally used on large-volume measurement and at town border stations.

In this anniversary year the continuing sense of duty to industry was expressed by William G. Hamilton's acceptance of the presidency of the Gas Appliance Manufacturers Association and by other acts of faith and works. He was also a director of the American Gas Association. John Ostler was currently first vice president of The Canadian Gas Association. Two World's Fairs were in the making: Century 21, to be held in Seattle, Washington, in 1962 and New York World's Fair 1964-1965, and all segments of the gas industry joined in these endeavors. George Stevenson was serving on the board of Century 21; Hamilton as executive vice president of Gas, Inc., formed expressly for the industry's participation in the New York event. The alliance was staunch and gas-tight.

For gas of the future, geologists exploring near Shiprock, New Mexico

Picture Credits

Index

Page numbers in italics indicate illustrations